FOR
Winifred Maud Gaitt & John Clark Murray
two real people

CONTENTS :

INTRODUCTION.

Looking back, it is difficult to gauge when the quest began. Quest: such a grand word; a search or pursuit, an undertaking with the purpose of finding or achieving a specific object. For me, the first step on the Charles I quest took place at lunchtime on Saturday, 17th August 1991. I was sitting in the Castle Tavern in St. Andrews waiting for an old school-friend, Jim Watson, and his son Ronan to appear. With them would be a married couple from Edinburgh, Bob and Lindsay Brydon. Bob, who was a historical researcher, had expressed an interest in meeting me, having heard of my previous experience in marine archaeology. At the meeting, Bob regaled me with the gist of a tale (part of which is contained herein) beginning with the Coronation visit of Charles I to Scotland in 1633 and culminating with the loss of a boat containing a large part of the King's household goods in the Firth of Forth. This proved to be the start of a long and continuing adventure which, to date, has culminated in the discovery of a wooden shipwreck and the publication of this book.

The original team; Bob, Alex Kilgour, Martin Rhydderch and I have had many trials and adventures of our own since then and over the years the small group has expanded with Ian Archibald and Carl Galfskiy joining and leading the offshore search.

But all that is another story. Throughout the whole process, the burning desire to tell the tale has been paramount. The following is, like Bob's previous book, (Charles I, His Scottish Coronation Visit, Robert & Lindsay Brydon, 1993) an attempt to do just that.

Through original research, I have gathered together a large number of the documents pertaining to the Coronation Visit. The definitive tome is still some years away. However, in order to release material in a more easily digestible form, this book was written. The first part is an historical novella, created out of my own imagination but based on the research material. I have made no attempt to replicate seventeenth century speech patterns and make no apologies for the poetic licence used and the inaccuracies that inevitably creep in.

The purpose is to entertain and to flesh out the lives of the ordinary folk in history who play a key role but whose names and lives have not been considered important enough to warrant attention. The second part of the book contains the appendices, basically, of all the relevant documents from the research material. They have been abridged and 'translated', where appropriate. The reader will see that all the characters, and the major events, in the novella existed and happened. Where I have 'invented', the inventions are within the realms of plausibility, and I hope the reader will concur. Those of you who have followed the project from the start may be perplexed by my story, particularly regarding the identity of the boat that sank. Was it 'The Blessing', one of the ferry-boats operating between Burntisland and Leith or one of the apparently unnamed baggage boats? The evidence uncovered so far is inconclusive and opinions vary. (Personally, I favour the latter.) I mention it here to account for some of the apparent indiscrepancies in the text. Research is a continuous process and all stories have their twists and turns. A reading of the appendices I trust will help account for this. I also hope the appendices will encourage others to delve into archives, local and central, and rediscover the 'real' people of history.

H.J.Murray

Palace of FALKLAND

FALKLAND PALACE . Slezor. (Nat. Lib. Scot.)

WEDNESDAY THE TENTH

CHAPTER 1.   Falkland, Dawn.

First light of day brought no respite from the rain, which had started the previous evening and continued all night without a break. James Clark squinted out from under his cloak; the smell of wet smoke had roused him from a short sleep. He was soaking and now, around him, a few fires were sputtering alight in the early mist. A number of the men, that had come with him from Creich were already up, hunched over a fire; willing it alight or preparing a breakfast of wet bread and ale. They were all soaking. The wagons they had driven down yesterday evening had afforded little protection from the incessant rain.

He could smell other fires and, in the mist, see other groups of huddled men; woollen cloaks, made heavy by the rain, hanging from them. All these little groups of men, with their carts and horses, were camped in forest clearings outside the small Fife village of Falkland. There, the Stewart kings had built a palace and, for hundreds of years, had used the surrounding forest as a hunting park. They had chosen well, the village lay snugly below two hills that protected it from the worst of weather, and the palace had grown with each succeeding monarch. The great forest, that once clothed nearly all of Fife, however had been greatly denuded over the centuries and now only around Falkland were there still tracts of ancient woodland large enough to be called a forest.

In the small clearings, James, his men from Creich, and a hundred other men had spent the night in the open in the pouring rain. They had come from as far east as Crail and St. Andrews and as far west as Rosyth and Dunfermline; these sodden men, each driving carts or leading a string of horses, all bound for Falkland at first light. It was to be the same routine as the week before, when the same groups had travelled to Dunfermline. Mercifully it had not rained that time.

All these men and horses shared a common purpose. At least they knew what to expect this time; the waiting, the queues and chaos and the arrogance of their hiring masters. Yet all these drenched Fife men were already old hands at shifting a King's baggage.

James could already see full carts and pannier-clad ponies leaving the gates of the Palace as they waited their turn in the queues of carts and horses which were lined up along the street. It was still raining and nobody seemed to appreciate the well dressed gentleman who periodically rode along the line exhorting everyone to keep as quiet as possible. His accent grated on these drenched souls.

"Quiet! His Majesty sleeps."

Perched high on his fine steed, an expensive horseman's coat and fine hat keeping him snug from the rain, his mount carried him, trotting, further down the line. The gentleman's prattle seemed greater than the clatter of harness, cart and the groans of a dozen Fifers combined.

"The devil to him," James cussed as he guided his cart into the courtyard of Falkland Palace. Before him all was activity but because of the rain, there seemed an effect of a slow dream-like quality to their movement. In almost total silence, dozens of men and young boys were dashing out of doors on all sides, all carrying bundles of some sort, sometimes two or three helped carry an especially large crate and heave it onto a cart. As one cart or string of pack horses were loaded in this way, these same groups would disappear back through the myriad of doors, reappear and load the next and so on until it was the turn of the men from Creich.

Meanwhile, back on the High Street, riding up and down the lines of wet waiting men and carts, Andrew Troughton, servant of his Majesty's silver scullery, was a happy man. Despite the rain, that had been pouring down even before they started that morning, (three in the morning - an unholy hour to start!) they were making progress; even amidst all the commotion of horses and carts in their hundreds; packing up, stowing crates and sacks. It had been organised chaos with everyone trying to make as little noise as possible, so as not to wake His Majesty.

No, despite the hovels with their wet beds and inedible food, that had been their lot since coming to this god-forsaken country; despite the bully Jasper Lindsay and his crony Atkinson and the packing and repacking of chests and crates, Andrew was a contented man. This was the penultimate load out. Two more nights in Edinburgh and then homewards at last.

Sitting astride a fair horse, even in the rain, he considered himself a lucky man. Nestled inside his doublet was fifty-five pounds, eleven shillings and three pennies; a good sum to have taken gaming, and maybe more to come tonight, back in Edinburgh. If he could only convince Ferries, Lysle and the others to play again, Ferries had money, he'd seen it that morning. It would just take a little bit of persuasion.

"Troughton, I thought you were keeping order here? Get back inside! His Majesty will be waking soon and you have duties."

In his reverie, Andrew hadn't noticed an older man rein his horse up beside him. It was Jasper Lindsay who was the "Cart-taker" in charge of the three carts belonging to the kitchens. The way he carried on, you would think they belonged to him, rather than the fact that they were his Majesty's carts supplied by the Tower and old Jasper merely signed for them. Three carts that had been packed and unpacked dozens of times already. At least it was near the end now and they would soon all be back in London, before the month was out, God willing.

"I'm going back now," replied Troughton.

He wheeled his horse around and returned through the gate as James Clark was leaving with a fully laden cart.

"Good luck to you, carter," cried Troughton to Clarke, in good humour.

"And precious little to you," Jim thought, as the wagon lurched into the street.

The smells of last night's banquet still hung in the warm air as Andrew Troughton entered the palace kitchens. Around him, all was activity; on one side kitchen boys were still feverishly packing wicker baskets with overlooked oddments; on the other, cooks and their assistants had already begun preparing His Majesty's first meal of the day. Seeking the warmest spot, he was in the process of pulling off his heavy leather coat and hanging it up to drip dry by one of the fires when he caught sight of John Lysle. It looked suspiciously like the man was trying to avoid him.

"Ah, John, are you going now? What about tonight in Edinburgh, another game?"

"You know I have no money left," replied Lysle. "You took mine as well as all the others. Look I have to go. See you at the ferry."

With that, the assistant cook gathered up a bundle and, facing the rain coming through the open door, dashed out. Andrew watched him as he stuffed the bundle into a pannier and then mounted a small pony. He gazed, snug in the kitchens as Lysle joined the writhing serpent of horses, men and carts as it snaked it's way out of the Palace gates and headed south. He would catch him at the ferry. They all had to wait for the King, and the King had to eat. So Andrew, a Kitchen cart and one from the Bedchamber and Wardrobe, would be among the last to leave Falkland. Ultimately it didn't matter. They all must wait for the King.

Between the two great hills, they climbed. It was hard going in the rain, but, once at the top, through the mist, Lysle could make out Fife stretched before him and south of the land, a strip of water; the Firth of Forth. Lysle could also see that to the west were blue skies and that, at last, the driving rain would let up. But right now, tramping down a road in the mud to some other little town.... Ah well, tonight in Edinburgh, maybe a good bed.

On the column squelched its way, gathering a heavy coating of Fife mud, occasionally passing a small village. The houses appeared to Lysle, and all the southerners in the train, more like cattle shelters than dwellings fit for humans. Peering out of doorways, near-naked children and tatter-clothed old women and men would stand and gawp as the endless procession dragged its way along the road south, ever onward in the wet.

"Lysle, can you hear me?" It was the voice of William Atkinson, Jasper's deputy. "The men with the panniers, keep them moving We have to be at the ferry and loaded before his Majesty arrives."

"Yes, sir."

With a pull on the reins, Lysle spurred his pony over to a group of men. They were struggling to control a string of pannier-clad ponies that had broken their traces.

"You," he yelled, "How far is it to the ferry?"

All of the dozen or so men were identically dressed in dark coloured woollen cloaks that afforded little protection against the rain. One of the group, helping a fallen comrade extricate himself from a tangle of wicker panniers and reins, turned. Lysle could see his face now, under the dripping folds of the hood; a Scottish face, ruddy with the ravages of many northern winters. The man was taller than the rest of his companions; taller than the average Scot, in fact.

"My name is James Clark," he announced. "I come from Creich. Neither I nor any of the men with me have ever been to Burntisland. Why don't you try that boy over there?"

With that James pointed over to yet another tired group, struggling with their animals.

"That lot are from Auchterderran. Bob Kilgour, that short man over there, he's been to Burntisland. And over the ferry. He told me this morning when we were loading. He'll know."

James Clark turned and busied himself retying the pannier ropes on one of the horses.

"Well you heard Mr. Atkinson, hurry up and get those animals moving."

You can never get a straight answer from any of them, Lysle thought as he pulled sharply on the reins, jerking his mount over to the other group.

"How far, Kilgour?"

"To Burntisland? Only a couple more miles now. You'll see it when we are over the next rise. We should be there by noon."

The rain had eased off and, over the next half an hour, it stopped completely. Brisk winds continued to play high in the sky, driving away the remaining clouds and allowing the sun to come through for the first time that day. All along the column, spirits picked up at the sight of the sun. Men like James Clark, who had been on the road the evening before, had travelled much further to make the Falkland rendezvous. Men, carts and horses from all over Fife and beyond; the column stretched back along the road for miles; miles of mud made worse by each passing cart. Once they arrived in Burntisland and had deposited their loads, they were free to go home. But until then, it was going to be all work and shoulders to the wheel. Lysle, having carried out his task, rode along the column looking for any of last night's gambling group. On top of one of the kitchen carts he caught sight of a pair of legs.

"John, I haven't seen you all day. I thought we'd left you behind."

The legs moved and the body of an elderly, fat man emerged from behind a large wooden crate.

"I wish you had. No more drink and cards for me, I'm a sick man. Whisky? You can keep it! Better I had kept to English beer."

He was sitting up now, jolting about as the cart hit rut after rut.

"Damn these roads! I'll not be happy till we're back in London."

Another pothole causes the cart to pitch alarmingly, nearly toppling the man off, and eliciting more groans.

"King's Master Cook, look at you. You'll need to smarten up by Burntisland. And tonight Andrew Troughton wants to play again. Better beer, better luck, eh?"

Lysle forced a grin of bravado.

"I don't know what you're smiling for, he cleaned you out. Don't look to me for money, I'm saving this," said Ferries, tapping his purse.

"Andrew will always find a few in the train and maybe some Scots who don't mind losing, but not me again."

John Ferries, the King's Master Cook, lay back down and tried unsuccessfully to ignore his hangover. Lysle looked back at the figure atop the cart. Plenty of time before tonight. Troughton will no doubt persuade him yet and digging his heels into the beast's flank he urged his mount forward.

The front of the column, now the sun was up, told a different story from the struggling men he had just left. It was a fine July afternoon now and, off to his left, on some higher ground, a sea of cornflowers drew him. Squinting now, in the bright sun, he could make out ahead, a small village tucked into a bay. He couldn't really see much of the village itself but, in the bay, fairly close inshore, the outline of a two-masted ship stood out in the sun. It was not as big as some he'd seen on the Thames but it looked good enough to carry him over the Firth of Forth.

On the northern leg of their trip, they had crossed the River Forth by the narrow bridge at Stirling but now he could see the great expanse of the Firth and the smoke of what must be Edinburgh, way off on the far bank. It looked a long way (not down to the village; they should be there in the hour) but over the water. When they were on the hills above Falkland it didn't seem so big, but now it looked a long way and an awful lot of water.

A Scotch Man

Firth of Forth (1790 chart). (Nat. Lib. Scotland.)

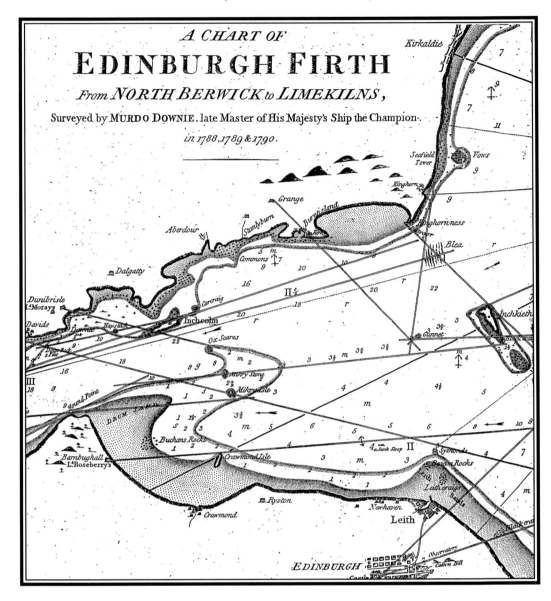

CHAPTER 2. Boats.

The wet marching men were only a few miles away from Burntisland and the sun was now high in the sky. The town lay drying now, sheltered in its bay, the imposing might of Sir Robert Melville's castle overlooking the harbour on its west side and the new parish church to the east. These two stone bastions together reflected the changing times in Scotland. The castle had seen glorious days but now its time had passed. The church however, had been built in the latest theological fashion in a common outpouring of religious fervour and had just started its role in history.

The thatched-roofed houses were steaming in the full sun as the town readied itself for a great event. Outside the solid stone tollbooth, which squatted resplendent, at the end of the High Street looking onto the harbour, the bailies were scurrying about, tending to last minute details. A greater commotion came from a large house in Midgait.

Running parallel to the High Street, and opening onto the harbour at its western end, Midgait was fronted on both sides by two-storey stone houses. The bright red, pantiled roofs made an imposing impression compared to the meaner thatched houses that made up most of the rest of the town. These grand houses were the homes of the wealthy merchants and shipowners of Burntisland, grown rich on trade with the continent and exotic lands far over the horizon. It was from outside one of these houses that the hubbub emanated.

A stout, oak door was ajar, the entrance punched through the thick stone wall that presented itself to the street. Through it four men, hot and sweaty, were struggling with huge coils of hemp rope. One was in late middle age but the others were much younger though all were dressed similarly, in loose breeches and shirt. The small hand cart, on to which the ungainly loads were destined, was already in danger of collapse from the folds of stiff new sailcloth that seemed to swamp it. One of the trio had had enough of hard work.

"Just away up to the gear store, and see what you can find. Damn, we could kit out another boat with this lot!" barked the elder figure. "Get in there and grab any double-blocks you see. Quick now and mind your tongue!"

The old man presented as a small weather-beaten figure, his skin oak brown from years in the Forth and beyond. The response was immediate as the disgruntled youth shucked his load and scuttled back into the gloom of the building.

"As soon as he's back, we must get down to the boat, before Captain Watson comes down and finds us still hanging about."

"He'll not be down for ages. He'll be up there preening himself."

They men turned their gaze upwards. The house, on its north face, presented a grim exterior. Apart from the pend gate where the sailors were loading their hand cart, the ground floor had only one other entrance. The second floor was pierced with two windows, both glazed. The top floor however had only two very small openings, to allow light to internal staircases.

Standing in a large room on the second floor of the house, was a middle-aged prosperous looking man. Clothed in what was obviously his finest outfit, the man admired the splendour of the decoration. The walls were ornately panelled and brightly painted. The ceiling too was painted, browns, reds, blacks and yellows in a geometric pattern of alternating crosses and octagons infilled with religious icons. On each cross was the face of a cherub encircled by a wreath of green leaves and red berries. The central octagons all bore the portraits of religious figures with Christ and the Lamb of God and Mary taking prominence. The other fifteen mostly held portraits of the ancient oracles.

The effect of the sunshine now streaming through the two large south facing windows on the coloured interior was inspiring and the man seemed lost in his own thoughts. But the moment was short-lived as a female voice sounded from another room.

"Hurry up, Andrew! Old Watt and some of the Blessing's crew have been taking gear all morning. You should be down there watching them. And your painter friend, James Workman, is below. He'll be looking for his silver."

Jolted from his reverie, Captain Andrew Watson, hurried down the few steps into the bedroom. There sat his wife, dressed simply in a dark-coloured woollen apron.

" My, Andrew Watson, you'll show up the King's men in those clothes. You're determined to look your best for his Majesty."

Watson planted a kiss on her lips and they embraced briefly. Then he had to leave his beloved Isobel and begin one of the most important days in his life. He crossed the passageway into another large room. Standing in the middle of it was a small man in his late forties. He appeared nervous; his hat clamped firmly between clenched fists.

"It's the money Captain Watson. I was wondering if you could see your way to…." The man's voice faltered and beads of sweat trickled down the nape of his neck. He fidgets with the collar of his coat and Watson seizes his opportunity.

"Good God, James, is it not for the glory of the Burgh and our King that everyone is working? I was just admiring your handiwork upstairs, you know. You were well paid for that. You'll get your money, never fret, but all in good time. We've not had a King here in fifteen years and you're moaning about some silver. Shame on you!"

The painter tried once more. "Your boat far outshines Captain Orrock's now. I thought perhaps something on account."

"Enough," replied Watson, "I've no time for this today. The baggage train will be here shortly and the King soon after. I've too much too do. See me next week."

And with those words James Workman, the painter, was ushered out of the room, through the main door and down the steps.

"Oh, and James!" Watson shouted down after him, "If any of my crew are hanging about the street gate, tell them to get down to the boat now."

Two great piers, crafted from stone blocks solid enough to survive the harsh winter gales, thrust out east and west. A one hundred-foot wide gap between them was the sole entrance into Burntisland harbour. The early afternoon sun glinted off the shallow water that barely covered its bottom. Fast against the town quay, two large broad-beamed boats lay tied up. In the Townhouse, a few hundred yards away, the bailies voices could be heard distinctly.

"I can see it from here. Why didn't Captain Orrock have his boat painted like Andrew's? It looks shoddy berthed there."

"You can ask him when he comes Bob. I think he thought, as Andrew Watson is going to take His Majesty and every other important person he can find onto the Blessing, there was no point in going to the additional expense."

"I haven't scrimped in providing wine for the reception."

"Aye, but that's you, Bobbie, that's you."

Their voices carried on the warm wind as, down on the quayside, the party that had been at Captain Watson's gear store were now offloading the hand cart. Hard against the quay the two boats were starting to lift as the rising tide began to flood in through the narrow harbour mouth. Both vessels were single-masted cargo boats used to carrying twenty to thirty tons of freight. They were tough, sturdy craft and, with a crew of nine, were the workhorses of the coastal trade. Both had seen hard usage but only one had recently received a total makeover, and it was into this boat that the hand-cart men were loading new rope and canvas.

"She looks grand with her new coat and this gear."

"Waste of money; all this just for one trip. And I'll bet nobody gets paid. Credit of the nation, bollocks."

"Ach Old Watt, it is a great honour. Don't be so miserable. At least it's stopped raining."

"Aye for the moment, but there's more in the west. It'll be here before we can get away."

"But the King himself will be on our boat. Is that not an honour?"

"It would be, if he'd brought any with him. But we get his placemen, like good Sir John Hay who sold out our fishing last year and sold out our parliament this. Aye some honour."

"Ah, you're a miserable sod, Old Watt. Lucky your son doesn't take after you."

The group carried on with their work while, on the other boat, a more relaxed regime seemed to prevail.

"Aye. You're dad has got them hard at it. Daft eejits, running about now. Wait until the baggage train arrives, then you'll see some work."

"How do you mean, Mr. Brown ?"

"Well, start adding it up, Jim. Ian Anderson went off last night with twenty horses and that was just the burgh. Henry Johnston, out at Newbigging, has gone off with at least fifty. All the other burghs from St. Andrews over to Dunfermline will be doing the same. Ian said when they were over in Dunfermline, to shift everything to Falkland, it was chaos. Hours of loading before they even got away. Everybody and their uncle giving orders. We'll be lucky to catch the tide."

"But we must catch the tide! Captain Orrock told me himself. We're transporting the King's baggage. It has to be in Leith tonight."

"Well , the King's baggage had better hurry up. The tide's turned now, we'll have to load and be out the harbour mouth by five o'clock."

"There's plenty of time, is there not ? We load cattle in an hour."

"Aye, but that's cattle."

William Brown, bosun of Captain Orrock's boat, having dispensed his words of wisdom, lay back on the deck, enjoying the warming sun, oblivious to the noise and activity around him. He'd seen too many harbours and too many sights to be worrying about a king on this glorious Scottish summer day. "Barbary", they knew him as, along the East Coast. Everyone hereabouts had their 'by-name' or nickname. Take his crew for instance; "Young Watt" because his father on the Blessing was "Old Watt"; the four Roberts; Harroware, Williamson, Wilson and Ennand, were respectively "Teuchter", "Big Huge", "Preacher" and "Slidam". John Gordon was known as "Red" and James Common, "Awfie". And William Brown was "Barbary"; the only man to have escaped the pirates in Algiers, returned home and without a penny given in ransom!

No work for Bosun Barbary and his crew yet. Let the others chase their tails - they would enjoy the sun.

Burnt Island.

Burntisland, Slezor. (Nat. Lib. Scot)

CHAPTER 3.   Backdykes, Women and Bairns.

All through the town, men were in a hurry. Baillies, like Robert Archison, off to check that the wine was ready for delivery to the Town Hall. Less prestigious, but just as important townsfolk, like John Brown the Baker, had been up all the night, like those on the baggage train, tending his ovens. At least he had been warm and dry. Now he hurried from the bakery with his assistant in tow, both laden with trays of freshly-baked bread. But though the men were busy, the town seemed somehow quiet. There were no women or children on the streets.

Inside one of the humbler houses, at the east end of the town on the north side of the High Street, sat two of the absent women. The open front door allowed them a view of the street beyond and every few minutes they could pick out the figure of a harassed artisan or a well-dressed baillie scurry by.

"Look at them, scuttling about full of themselves. And us banned from going outside. It's stupid, Janet. Mark my words, the men will make a mess of it."

The young woman turned her attention from the activity outside to her companion; a woman older than herself, who was content to enjoy the occasion and not worry about matters that she had no control over.

"And Master Christie is trying to do the impossible and hold the children in school the entire day," she continued, warming now to the subject. Her friend offered her own view on the day's events.

"Well, Elspeth, at least it's a day off. And one day less of Barbary coming round all moonfaced. The boats won't be back till tomorrow, so we can take things easy."

Janet Mair winked at her friend Elspeth conspiratorially. She knew that while Elspeth was semi-officially engaged to Barbary Brown, (bosun of Orrock's boat and a prize catch!) she was seeing someone else; an old flame from the past. But with Barbary busy on his Royal duties all today and away overnight she should have been free to meet him. If it wasn't for the ban.

"Bobby will be waiting for me. This ban is ridiculous; all women and children to be off the streets from dawn to dusk or eight days jail - it's criminal!" They both laughed at the absurdity of Elspeth's words, but Janet detected a hint of desperation in her tone.

Elspeth Coasin's old flame, Robert Tough, had turned up, out of the blue, over a month ago. Elspeth had been with him when he had worked on the boats along the Fife coast, before he left to make his fortune in London. Now he seemed to be skulking, or so Janet thought, and always wanted to meet in secret. Elspeth said he had come back to be near Dysart, and to be near his parents and her. Yet he was always vague about his time down south.

Janet could see why Elspeth had fallen for him again; the feeling of danger and excitement. Poor old dependable Barbary didn't have much of a chance. Elspeth should have told him weeks ago. It was not fair; he was a good man, William Brown. A fine man and he'd had his share of dangers too. Wasn't he Bosun Barbary, the man that tricked the Turkish pirates and come home to tell the tale; the brave sailor who had once saved the baker's son when he fell overboard by holding him and swimming for over a mile to the shore? Elspeth would be mad to throw up a man like that for a slippery eel of a rascal.

"I'm going out," said Elspeth suddenly. "I don't care if it is eight days! I'll go by the backdykes. Nobody will notice. They're all caught up with the King." With that she grabbed her shawl and was out the back door before Janet could react.

"Don't be a fool," she cried but it was too late. She watched as Elspeth ran down the rig to the backdyke gate, opened it quickly and disappear through it. She could follow her, in her mind's eye, along the backdykes, then across the Kirkton Road to the copse beside the mill dam. Bobby would be waiting for her there. A normal day was bad enough but today with a King coming and all the Baillies out and about, she was courting calamity.

On the hill overlooking the harbour stood the parish church, its square form topped by a central tower. The Bishop of London, William Laud, had already insulted the parishoners, the week before, by likening it to a pigeon house! But today all was peace. Inside, the central pulpit was empty but above the seating in one of the box pews was Captain Watson and another man. Both were silent, lost in their thoughts. Captain Watson was the first to break their contemplation.

"It's been a bad business from the start, Captain Orrock. This coronation and parliament has been a bad business. Poor Sir Robert Melville having his name taken by the King and the Earl of Rothes too. It's no good for Fife!"

"It's not Fife we should be worried about but Scotland itself and our Church," replied Orrock. "I don't think his Majesty is aware of our love for it's freedoms. I, for one, will not see that taken away and there are plenty like me who'll fight to keep it."

"Hold your tongue, Captain Orrock. Men have lost their heads for less."

The good captain declined to reply and the two men returned to their silent prayers; prayers for a successful voyage today and a peaceful country in the future. Outside the thick stone walls, the town's male citizens rushed to complete last minute details. But, like the women, the children too had been banned from venturing outside and so tucked in beside the church, a small building reverberated with the sound of young voices.

Thomas Christie, schoolmaster of the burgh, is having a particularly difficult day, his charges are unimpressed with Latin and Arithmetic. The exasperation and rising anger shows in the tone of his voice.

"John Watson, your father shall hear of your disobedience!"

The small boy does not hear his teacher, his thoughts are on Kings, Lords and his father's boat; much more exciting business than the unwanted grind of learning by rote.

CHAPTER 4.   Baggage at the Harbour.

The townsfolk – even those indoors – heard the clatter of the approaching baggage for several minutes before anything came into sight; the sound of mens' voices, cajoling and cursing, horses and ponies whinnying in the wind and the dull rumbling of cartwheels, still caked in trail muck. But then the head of the baggage train was at the Kirkton gate, spilling down the steep hill and into the High Street. Heads were at every window, straining to see the cause of the din. Soon it seemed that horses and carts were filling every corner of Burntisland. The Tollbooth was an island bastion in a sea of wagons and horses; the steam from their nostrils and sweating flanks mingling with that being blown from the warming stone walls. The whole of the street stank of sweat, horse-breath and muck. So thick it was that even the strong sea breeze could not carry it away. Indeed it seemed to cling to clothes and nostrils as if it had a life of its own.

All of the heavily laden carts; all the horses with their back-chafing panniers were led by exhausted men who had only one thought: to finish the job and fall into their own bed that night. All had one destination: two boats secured to the quayside, one gaily painted, the other less so. To the men with the horses, they looked big and, as they passed down their loads, they were grateful to have discharged their duty. The boat's crews too were happy. Bosun Barbary had worried earlier about catching the tide but now it seemed that soon they would be fully loaded and bound for Leith. The sailors worked quickly to stow the chests and bundles.

He'd been right to save his crew. Now the like of Awfie and Preacher were grafting hard as bundle after bundle came down. And there were carts too, going to Leith. They were a suprise to both bosuns. They looked like giant wooden chests with cartwheels attached. All the way from London they had come and now they were set to journey all the way back. Barbary had Young Watt, Slidam and Red improvise a ramp similar to the one they used for cattle, by laying spars and spare timber from the quay down into the hold of the vessel. Both crew's sweated and cursed as they used these jury-rigged ramps to run the Tower Carts, as the royal servants called them, into the holds. But as time wore on and more Fife carts had emptied, their mood changed.

"How much more stuff ?" Barbary shouted to John Lysle who was standing at the quayside with a party of royal servants including John Ferries. All the servants, who had come with the baggage train, had milled about and generally got in the way during the loading.

"You're part of this, are you not? How much more gear?" repeated Barbary.

"How dare you speak to me in that tone, sailor!" barked John Lysle. "Did you hear the insolence of the man, Mr. Ferries? How much more stuff? Well, it's hard to say, quite a bit I should think. And there's the carts still to come with his Majesty. But no matter how much more there is, you will do as you are told!"

Lysle was, if anything, more concerned than Barbary. The ship in the bay had turned out to be His Majesty's pinnace provided by the Earl of Linlithgow. He and all the baggage were to travel to Leith on these two much smaller boats (much too small, in his opinion). But ,worried or not, he was not going to have some lowlife sailor talk to him in such a manner.

"More carts! For Christ's Sake how many more are there?" cried Barbary in exasperation.

"You insolent cur," retorted Lysle. "Kitchen, Wardrobe, His Majesty's carts for the morning, you'll take what comes and be honoured to do it. I'll have no more of your tongue, Scotsman!"

But Barbary was no longer listening to the prattling of some jumped-up hireling, he had to do something.

"No, this is no good. I'm going to find Captain Orrock."

The worried bosun leapt up onto the quay and disappeared into the crowd. Pushing his way through the mass of horses and empty carts he started up the High Street. The way was clearer now as the carts were formed up in orderly line as they made their way out of the town by the east gate. A small jam had been caused by a couple of men trying to hold a train of pannier horses still when Barbary came up. One of them was Jim Clark. The sight of more unloaded panniers only served to increase Barbary's fears.

"More damned stowage! Why are you not at the harbour with the rest, adding to the pile?" he snapped.

Taken aback by the ferocity of the outburst, Jim Clark spouted his excuses.

"I'm finished with all that and away home. I'm only doing some Dysart men a good turn holding these. One of them spotted a fugitive lying with a woman across at the millpond, they're off to catch him."

The leading pony of the string shied as a cartsman tried to edge around the group causing Jim Clark to fall heavily. His friend sprang forward to help him. Barbary would have offered his aid but couldn't spare anymore time. He had to find Captain Orrock and put a stop to the loading.

"If they catch the woman and she's local, it's prison for her too," he shouted as he left Jim Clark and his friend and ran up the High Street. He continued right into Kirkgate, hoping to catch Captain Orrock as he came down from the parish church.

And there he was, at the corner of Midgait, speaking to Captain Watson. Good, he could talk to them both.

"Captain Orrock, Sir!"

"Aye, Barbary, shouldn't you be down supervising the loading? It's a responsible job. I always expect the best from you."

"That's just it, Sir, there's too much freight. I'm afraid the boat won't take it. The royal servants insist we load it all."

Captain Orrock coloured slightly at the implied slight to his boat, particularly with Captain Watson standing right beside him. The senior Captain seized his opportunity.

" You're boat can't take it, eh Orrock? I was right to use the Blessing to take his Majesty's party out to the pinnace. You don't see any of my men come bleating about sinking boats. Aye, and you Barbary , you're not frightened of some boxes and a few soft southerners."

Barbary felt it only right to say something in his employers defence, especially as he had caused this loss of face.

"But surely Captain Watson, if you are taking His Majesty, it means we must take all his carts and both boats are near full laden now."

Watson brushed aside all argument with his usual sweeping assurances.

"There will be room enough for everything, be assured. Captain Orrock and I will be down at the quayside to supervise and I will be personally greeting his Majesty and seeing off both boats, nothing can go wrong."

Captain Orrock, seeking to regain lost ground, leapt to his senior's support.

"Yes, that's right, William, everything will be all right. Now back to the harbour to your duties and let Captain Watson and I attend to ours."

The two shipmasters, resplendent in their finery, turned and hurried off towards the High Street to do their civic duty. Barbary, suitably humbled, walked back down Midgait and returned to the harbour.

The quay was quieter now. Groups of royal servants were still milling about shouting orders at departing packmen and carters but the loading itself had all but ceased. On the Blessing, Bosun Smith was giving his crew no let up as they busied themselves cleaning the deck and generally tidying up. Barbary's crew were waiting for him as he stepped on board.

"What did he say," enquired a hand.

Bosun Barbary was about to reply with the same soothing words of Captain Watson but suddenly the activity on the dock and in the holds of the two boats stopped. Everyone heard it together. The sound of trumpets. That sound could only mean one thing. The King had arrived in Burntisland.

A Highland Man

CHARLES I. Van Dalen. ^(Nat. Lib. Scot.)

The high & mighty Monarch CHARLES by y^e grace of GOD king of Great Brittaine France & Ireland Defendor of the Fayth. etc.

EDYNBURGH

C^o: v: Dalen sculp: Sould by Tho: Ienner at the Exc:

CHAPTER 5.   King Charles in the Burgh.

The first ceremony took place at the Kirkton gate. Captain Watson was there, as were all the baillies. Robert Galbraith, their spokesman, was giving a long rambling speech. Watson, who had been in Edinburgh at the time of the King's entry to the capital, noticed that, not only were the King and his Lords more soberly dressed now, but also that several were talking among themselves all the way through Galbraith's speech - and his Majesty seemed downright bored!

The King and his nobles, with the baillies in attendance, then proceeded to pass among the ordinary townspeople. Looking strangely incongruous on their magnificent steeds, all silks and velvets, they headed towards the Tollbooth. Men lined the streets and every window was filled with the faces of women, all anxious to steal a glimpse of their king. King Charles looked magnificent, outshining even the most fashionable of his courtiers. But for the crowds in the street and the faces at the windows there was little time to take it all in.

For once inside the Tollbooth, King Charles and his entourage were only seen by the baillies. And even that was not for long. The Marquis of Hamilton had already singled out Captain Watson and was pressing him to hurry with the loading and allow the King to leave. They would sample some wines and listen to some more speeches while the two boats were receiving their final cargoes but it was easy to see the royal party were keen to depart.

"Hallo! So we meet in Burntisland," cried Andrew Troughton to Lysle and Ferries who were now at the quayside. He jumped down from the cart that had just arrived. He'd spotted them from his vantage point and was now walking gingerly across a gangplank onto the boat to join them.

"The other one looks the better boat, if you ask me. At least it's been painted," he proferred.

"Nobody asked you Troughton! And obviously His Majesty is going on that boat. We're on this." John Ferries pointed down to the wood of the deck they were standing on.

"And it's already full, I heard one of the crew say so," John Lysle added, eyeing the cart Andrew had just alighted from and the others now ranged alongside.

"Full or not, the carts of the King and me, Andrew Troughton, are joining you for a sail in Scotland."

Bosun Barbary heard the bravado of Andrew Troughton with disgust.

Wait till he's halfway over and he won't be so bold, mused Barbary. "Him and his damn carts," he muttered below his breath.

But there was nothing for it. He had been told by them all; Watson, Orrock, those pompous servants. 'A King's cart goes where a King goes,' he mimicked as they roped the first of the carts and swung it over onto the deck. He cried out to Young Watt and Awfie to lash them down well. His crew knew the reason for his haste, for the tide was rising fast and time was now short.

On a day crammed with activity, on the Blessing, they could only wait for their final cargo. It was a welcome respite for the weary crew. Several took the chance too snatch a moment's sleep but one on board had his eyes wide open. They were fixed on the sight of another large wooden cart as it was hoisted into the air. Old Watt's eyes watched keenly as his son guided it down. He too was worried. The Blessing was well loaded but John Smith, the bosun, had been under orders to keep the deck clear for the King and his party. So now he fretted as the last of the carts was stropped and prepared for its open-air voyage onto the other boat; his son's boat. They could have at least put one on the deck of the Blessing.

But the time for worrying had past. The King and his party had left the Tollbooth and, with Captain Watson leading, were now at the quayside. The bailies, despite earlier hints, insisted on continuing the 'official' reception. Unfortunately, again, the King was not in the slightest bit interested and, amid scenes bordering on farce, the Royal Party boarded the Blessing. Royal servants were also jumping onto the vessel, desperate not to be left behind, among them the gamblers which Andrew Troughton had managed to solicit.

In a trice, Smith was shouting orders, the Blessing was under sail and had cleared the harbour mouth. Old Watt would have looked back, anxious for his son, but he was an experienced sailor and now that they were in open water and heading for the pinnace anchored in the Roads, he could see something that concerned him even more. From out of the west, a dense black carpet was rapidly unrolling itself down the widening expanse of the river. The old mariner knew what it was and a shiver ran through him. A storm was barrelling down the Forth and it would be on them in minutes!

A Scotch Woman

CHAPTER 6.   Sinking.

Back at the harbour, they were oblivious to the approaching danger. Everyone was preoccupied with loading and getting underway on the second baggage boat before the tide turned. Andrew Troughton's party had swelled to over twenty; cooks like John Ferries and John Lysle and others desperate to be with the King tonight in Edinburgh. They were standing on the deck in groups of three and four with Troughton flitting between them still trying to drum up more players for the gaming that night.

"Some of you will have to go below and lie on the cargo, we can't work the boat with all these people on deck," cried Barbary, hoarsely.

They had to leave. Now! Feverishly, Awfie, Red, Preacher and Slidam worked the main sheet and, quickly, they were under sail and away. The Blessing was already pitching and yawing in the choppy water as she felt the first slashing rain that heralded the awesome fury of the approaching storm. The King's group on the deck were becoming increasingly alarmed. Just a short stretch separated the Blessing, which was now dropping heavily into each trough, from the King's pinnace. The Lord High Admiral of Scotland had spent his money well, for the pinnace, while obviously affected by the worsening storm, was riding the seas with ease. On her lee side the water was calm and offered a welcome respite to the Royal party. Within minutes, though (it must have seemed hours to the King), they were alongside. Members of the Court, who had transferred earlier, watched in desperation as the two crews struggled to keep the boats alongside one another. Anxious courtiers rushed to help the King and his party scramble across to safety. After a rapid (if somewhat inelegant) boarding the Blessing pulled away. All left on board her heaved a sigh of relief; the King was safe. Captain Watson's boat could have taken the King over to Leith, but it would be a choppy ride. The crew still had a cargo and twenty-odd frightened servants onboard; a great responsibility. But they also had other more immediate responsibilities to their fellow mariners. For now their thoughts turned to the other boat which was rapidly getting into difficulty.

"The devil with this," cursed the bosun. Barbary knew they were in trouble as soon as the overladen boat had cleared the harbour. Now, nine, ten foot waves pounded the side of the vessel. As each crest hit, the boat would pitch alarmingly. The carts were skidding and straining against the lashings Awfie was desperately adding.

"Get clear Awfie, it's going!" cried the bosun but as the wind tore Barbary's cry from his mouth, one of the carts burst its fastenings, toppled, and crashed over the side, taking a section of railing with it. The boat bucked and rolled as the weight of the cargo shifted. Young Watt made a grab for Awfie as he lost his footing and careered across the deck towards the gash made by the cart. Somehow they both made it to the masthead.

"Do something!" The terrified voice of John Ferries boomed uselessly from his stout frame. He was jammed half-way through the stern hatch. Below, Andrew Troughton, John Lysle and a score more terrified servants of his Majesty cowered. Before he could speak again, the boat pitched and Ferries was sucked out of the hatch and thrown onto the flooding deck.

"Grab that rope, or you're a dead man!" Young Watt shouted, but it was useless. Whether he heard above the roar of the waves or not, it hardly mattered; the next wave hit and the entire deck was awash. John Ferries was swept over the side as the wave passed through. But the boat was rapidly filling through the open hatch and, in a moment, the next wave was upon them.

"Save yourselves, she's going!" warned Barbary , at the top of his voice.

Young Watt barely heard his bosun's voice and he couldn't see him, for suddenly the deck was no longer beneath his feet. He was in the water and the freezing blackness and the lashing surf. And the boat's cargo was no longer beside him but all around him. Flailing the water, he could feel the debris surround him; pieces of rigging, ropes, wicker baskets and a wooden cart spiralling down into the depths below him.

Then he was in a dream. There was Barbary chasing grinning, royal servants down the High Street of London. He and the rest of the crew were all sitting on carts, laughing at them and eating fine food. But it was cold in this dream and dark. Bitter cold and blind darkness. Instinctively, he started to pray for his father and the King. Unable to tell whether or not his eyes were open, he became aware that his shipmates were all gone. He knew he'd join them soon.

"The Mariner"

29

CHAPTER 7.   Aftermath, Leith and Dusk.

In Burntisland the sun is setting. The marvellous and tragic events of the day are being talked about all through the town. Eye-witnesses are already telling their tales. Tonight it is their wives and children who sit in rapt silence as legends of how a King and his Lords were saved from shipwreck but were powerless to act as his riches sank to a watery grave. In the weeks to come the tales will get more elaborate as the teller seeks to impress his audience. But not all storytellers seek recompense in return for a good yarn. Some have lost loved ones. Two men were eye witnesses only to a tragedy.

"You said nothing could go wrong Andrew. I've lost a boat, a good crew and the finest bosun I ever had."

"Aye, it's been a bad business all round, James, your boat gone, His Majesty gone leaving nothing but bad trouble behind him. I'm sure the Blessing pulled at least one person out, I'll lay it was Barbary. Your bosun has a charmed life. Of the others, the King's men are with their Maker now but some of your crew could have been carried down the coast and still turn up. We'll find out tomorrow when the Blessing gets back. Maybe it would have been better if she had gone down instead. We may all regret her being the better boat." Captains Watson and Orrock console each other and inevitably turn their thoughts to the future.

Across town, Elspeth Coasin and Janet Mair sat and watched the fading light.

"You were very lucky not to have been caught, Elspeth," Janet scolded, her matronly ways given full flood. Elspeth however was unrepentant.

"They were more interested in catching Bobby and serving His Majesty, than chasing a mere lassie like me. Anyway they gave up when they saw they couldn't reach him. They couldn't catch a forkie in a tar-bucket. No, he's long gone now. Aberdeen and the continent, he said." And then, with a sigh, "So it's Barbary Brown for me."

Janet couldn't believe her friend's fickleness and sought to bring her down to earth. "But the boat's gone Elspeth, with everybody on it. And a king's ransom, they say."

But Elspeth Coasin was not a woman to allow reality to intefere with her plans.

"No," she replied, "Not my Barbary. He'll be on the Blessing or fetched up on the coast somewhere. He'll be back here tomorrow with a story to tell. You wait and see."

Janet would wait and see. But she would also pray that night for Barbary.

A slight, almost imperceptible, rocking motion and the sound, far, far off, of men and horses came creeping into Young Watt's mind. Then the sound of a man's voice intruded from behind the horses clatter, at first vague but then clearer.

"Hot whisky! Pour it down his throat. Hot whisky, cured me of the drowning, when I was in Bergen."

Young Watt was drifting in and out of his dream again. He could see Barbary and the King drinking together but this time it was different. He felt warm, his throat felt warm and then his belly. He opened his eyes. He was in the stern cabin of a boat, lying on a makeshift bed; just a couple of sea chests with a spare sail thrown over. The heavy oak beams, above his head, smelled familiar and he thought of Barbary, Big Huge, Red, Awfie Common and the rest and then suddenly he was afraid again. There was panic in his eyes and he reached out for something solid. He felt the warm strength of a man's arm and held on. It was his father's arm. He saw him smiling and could make out Dave Murray hovering anxiously behind. This wasn't his boat. His boat was gone. He was on the Blessing.

"I'm not dead?" he croaked.

"No, good luck to you. But that's the best of it. We think the rest are all gone, son."

The father poured a drop more whisky from a steaming jug while David Murray took up the story.

"We could see you were in trouble so, after we delivered His Majesty, we tacked round just as the boat foundered. The seas were like mountains."

And so David Murray related to the young man how The Blessing had tacked across the teeth of the gale, horrified as their sister ship had taken the waves on her broadside. They had watched helplessly as the first cart broke loose and crashed through the side. The sea, exploiting the weak spot, had flooded over and into the boat. Then suddenly all that there was, was a strangely calm patch of surface, pocked with debris. All eyes had scanned the water as the Blessing came round.

"There! By the cask!"

One of the crew had thrown a grapple, nagging the shapeless bundle as it pitched in the waves; a hard pull and they had it on deck. It was Young Watt and he was alive!

Though they had still searched on, desperate for signs amid the broken timber, of other survivors, the seas had been against them. Only once again did a cry ring out.

"There's Barbary! Over there!"

But then he was gone. They weren't even sure it was Barbary and there was no more time. Although the storm was clearing as rapidly as it had come, the sea had defeated them. They could do nothing more and had a landfall at Leith to make before the tide turned again.

A great rumbling sound of iron wheelhoops on cobblestones coupled with the shouts of men and the clatter of horses abruptly ended David Murray's tale. Old Watt glowered.

"Those damn carts, I wish they were all at the bottom of the Forth."

"You're son doesn't know, Old Watt. There was a right panic on when we docked. The King had already gone but his servants were onboard the Blessing even before we could tie up. They are trying to work out who and what was on board when she went down. They'll want to talk to you."

"That can wait until the morrow, Davie. My laddie's not well,"

As the light starts to fail, all over Fife men are arriving home in the gathering gloom. Dog tired, but burning with the events of the day, they bed their animals down for the night. All they want is a warm bed and sweet sleep but all have a tale to tell their loved ones; a tale of how a king's ransom and God knows how many lives were lost on that day in the treacherous Firth. Wednesday the tenth.

Detail. Return of the Dutch East Indies fleet, May 1599. Andries Van Ertvelt. (Nat. Maritime. Mus.)

(The three vessels shown may illustrate the types used on the tenth of July. The human figures are painted larger than scale.)

DUKE OF HAMILTON, 1633. Myten.(Scot. Nat.
Portrait. Gal.)

Charles I and son (James II)

BURNTISLAND Town Map

PART 2

HISTORICAL SOURCES

Introduction

When Bob Brydon brought the story to me I was excited not by the cargo being carried by the ill-fated vessel but rather by the circumstances and location of the wreck. My background being primarily archaeology and for the last twenty odd years the majority of my work has been in Marine Archaeology. The story fascinated me on technical grounds. The vessel had capsized and sunk a short distance from a working harbour within a relatively sheltered estuary. More importantly, within a hundred mile radius of the site are all the skills necessary to locate and recover an historic wreck. The utilisation of all the computing and offshore skills built up in Scotland over the last forty years would be required if we were going to have a chance at locating any wrecks. The "King Charles Wreck" story appeared to offer the ideal opportunity. From the outset it was realised, that an investigation, however time consuming, of the written evidence, was essential. On a purely practical level, any information that enabled the Project group to pinpoint the search area and provide detail in regard to size and type of vessel would lessen the costs involved in mounting offshore search operations. However the unearthing of historical records is a time consuming business and with no funding, other than from within the group, the operation was *painful*.

Where others have spent entire careers immersed in the intricacies of Stuart history. My research has only touched on a few months of his reign and I would make no claims as to the level of my knowledge of the period. As the project gathers pace I hope that further volumes can be produced to explore other aspects of the Coronation journey in more detail. For the purposes of the current work I have tried to keep to events and activities that have relevance to the day of the sinking. The appendix contained below represents only a small part of the Coronation Journey information recovered with yet more still to be sourced. The method I used in the research programme was to start at the most readily available information and work outwards from there. Bob Brydon had pointed to the event detailed in Spalding's account. From that brief account it is possible to develop several strands of research.

Geographical places - Falkland, Burntisland, Leith and Edinburgh.
People - King Charles, servants, boat crews.
Objects - ships, baggage, etc.

The Stuart period in many respects represents the beginnings of the modern world. Though superstition and ignorance was to allow witch trials for another century the stage was set for the world we are familiar with today. Limited companies had been trading since Elizabethan times and discoveries in North America had opened up new business opportunities. The continuing rise of management and literacy contributed to the relatively large amount of archive material still surviving from that period.

Many hours, days, weeks, months and finally years were spent visiting libraries, public record offices and private houses tracking down documents. The documents, once found are extremely difficult to read as the illustration contained within this book illustrates. The search is very much like a detective mystery; the trail is peppered with clues and red herrings. A great deal of perseverance and a little luck are the main tools. I have found no evidence of a 'Court of Inquiry' into the sinking. The fragments are scattered within existing documents and the teasing out is fraught with danger. The paper search continues.

TROUGHTON, (Traquair House) see footnote 15.

A note of wigt & coat yat mr Andrew Troughton
one of his maiesties seruantis of the siluer smeddorie
had on whan hee was cast away in scotland
the 9th of July 1633 : / viz

one peese mashe roabe of wateryt collor & lace
wt silke & siluer buttons

his dublett & hoese of r lace noune wt the collor
of his roabe the dublett had edged buttons
& the hoese weare pered longes all the
toope abouts and frng or some thing more wt
a little darker collor r lace)

for his eyes hee wai of a midd longe eyes
the beard of his head was blacke & the eard
of his beard a light browne

50 or 60 pounds in money that he
had about him when he was cast
away

The Sinking

Information on the sinking is very sparse. As I will suggest, King Charles was returning quickly to London after a less than successful Scottish visit and the sinking, I suspect, was yet another unlucky incident that he wished to put behind him. I have found no evidence of salvage attempts at the time and shortly after, larger events in history swept away the King and memories of the incident. The accident is mentioned in three historical accounts; all the writers being contemporary to the incident though each of the accounts was written after the event. We may assume that Sir James Balfour's Annals[1] is the most accurate as he was intimately connected to the Coronation journey. John Row [2] was minister of the Church in Carnock near Dunfermline only some ten miles from Burntisland whereas John Spalding[3] was an ecclesiastical lawyer attached to St Machar's in Aberdeen and would be the least likely to have received first-hand accounts. However the three accounts show a marked level of agreement with the only major difference being the number of people involved. One reason for this is possibly Sir James Balfour use of the word servant to include only senior personnel, coupled with a degree of exaggeration of the numbers before the story reached the ears of John Spalding. More reliable are the mentions of the accident by Court personnel at the time. Again there are three, so far discovered; William Laud[4] (Bishop of London, Archbishop of Canterbury August 1633) was a senior member of the Coronation party but not with the King on the day of the sinking. Sir John Coke[5] had been one of the two Secretaries of State since Charles had come to the throne and accompanied Charles throughout the Coronation journey. We may assume he was with the King at Burntisland. The other writer, Viscount Conway and Killultagh,[6] was also with the party at Burntisland. One more indirect mention of the accident appears in the papers relating to the erection of a lighthouse on the May Island,[7] (actually the first lighthouse in Scotland).

From these various sources we can conjecture the sequence of events. The king's ship/pinnace was lying in Burntisland Roads. Two boats left Burntisland harbour, the king being in the leading vessel; both boats ran into difficulties after encountering a sudden squall. The leading boat managed to rendezvous with the ship/pinnace and the king transferred. The boat following after, containing twenty to thirty people and a quantity of the king's baggage, foundered.

What of the boats, the victims and the cargo? The three vessels concerned have been discovered in the records. Firstly the king's ship/pinnace[8] must have been of a fair size. The terms "bark" and "pinnace" [9] were used in a general sense to describe sailing vessels, while "ship" is a term for an ocean going vessel. We can assume the vessel supplied by the Lord High Admiral was at least two masted and capable of carrying a large number of passengers. The two other boats mentioned appear to be used for cargo transportation between Burntisland and Leith[10]. The term ferryboat is possibly somewhat misleading in that they may not have been purpose built ferries but rather boats that were ferrying cargo between two points. Their supply by Burntisland shipowners with details of the crew[11] indicate two similar size vessels each manned by a nine man crew. The harbour at Burntisland had been used as a ferry point[12] and continued as such until the Railway Bridge was built over the River Forth in the 19th Century. As the harbour dried at low tide the boats could only leave on a high tide, which on the tenth of July 1633 was five o'clock in the afternoon[13]. We can assume that these two vessels were between fifty and seventy feet in length and fifteen to twenty feet in breadth with a carrying capacity of between sixty to a hundred tons. They may have had the ability, as later boats had, of running cargo down a ramp into the hold. The fact that two Burntisland shipowners were involved in the supply of the boats leads me to the supposition that it was Captain Orrock's boat that was lost. Captain Watson was the senior shipowner in Burntisland and I would assume he would want the privilege of carrying the King. I have yet to discover a possible name for this boat (the majority of Captain Watson's boats were called 'Blessing's) or if Captain Orrock was recompensed for his loss.

The victims are more difficult to find. One name came from the Burntisland records[14], that of King's Cook, John Ferries, who was washed ashore near Burntisland some weeks later. I was always intrigued as to how the citizens of Burntisland were able to identify the body until the archivist at Traquair House showed me the Andrew Troughton note[15]. The existence of this note suggested that there had been an attempt made at the time to make arrangements for the aftermath of the accident. Presumably similar notes were prepared for many of the victims as an aid to identification and distributed to the villages along the Forth. I am hopeful other notes will turn up. The King's Master Cook, John Ferries, appears in other documents (see Coronation chapter) but it is his appearance in the Jewel House papers[16] that is the more interesting. The Jewel House was situated in the Tower of London and held all the Crown's Plate and jewellery including the Crown Jewels. The Keeper of the Jewel House obviously kept detailed records regarding the issue of items. At this time the incumbent was a Sir Henry Mildmay. It is within these lists that more victims appear. One John Lysle[17], an assistant cook, is mentioned. There is also an intriguing list with those deceased marked[18]. The deceased position within the king's household tallies well with the description of the victims in the accounts. In the accounts as seen there is mention of two survivors. I suggest that it is probable that these would be crew members rather than passengers. The ability to swim was rare in the 17th century!

The Jewel House records also allow us to look at the baggage/cargo of the boats. One entry is particularly intriguing[19] as it shows a complete issue of a dinner service to the Scullery. As we have seen, Andrew Troughton was a servant of the Silver Scullery and it is possible this was a replacement for a service lost in the accident. The existence of carts, also issued from the Tower of London, has been established (see Coronation chapter) but it is a list made out in August 1633[20] that is of more relevance to the sinking. I have left only the carts (There were, in fact, twenty-three not returned) that tally with the accounts, the positions of the known victims and those individuals known to have been present. Certain carts may have been taken by their assignees to their country home prior to a return to London. A further note[21] suggests carts were still missing late in the year. The size of the baggage train can be estimated from the numbers of horses ordered for each move (see Coronation chapter) and must represent a total weight in excess of one hundred tons.

We can conclude, then that a vessel sank on Wednesday the 10th of July 1633. The size of the vessel and its carrying capacity is adequate to ferry part of the Baggage Train and a number of passengers to Leith. The identity of the victims known and the existence of carts attached to their department within the Royal Household which had not returned to London by August, suggests that the cargo was primarily Kitchen/Dining equipment and possibly The Wardrobe. The carts themselves may have contributed to the vessel's loss, their bulk acting to render the boat unstable.

JEWELHOUSE PAPERS, (Somerset Records Office)

see footnotes 16 and 17

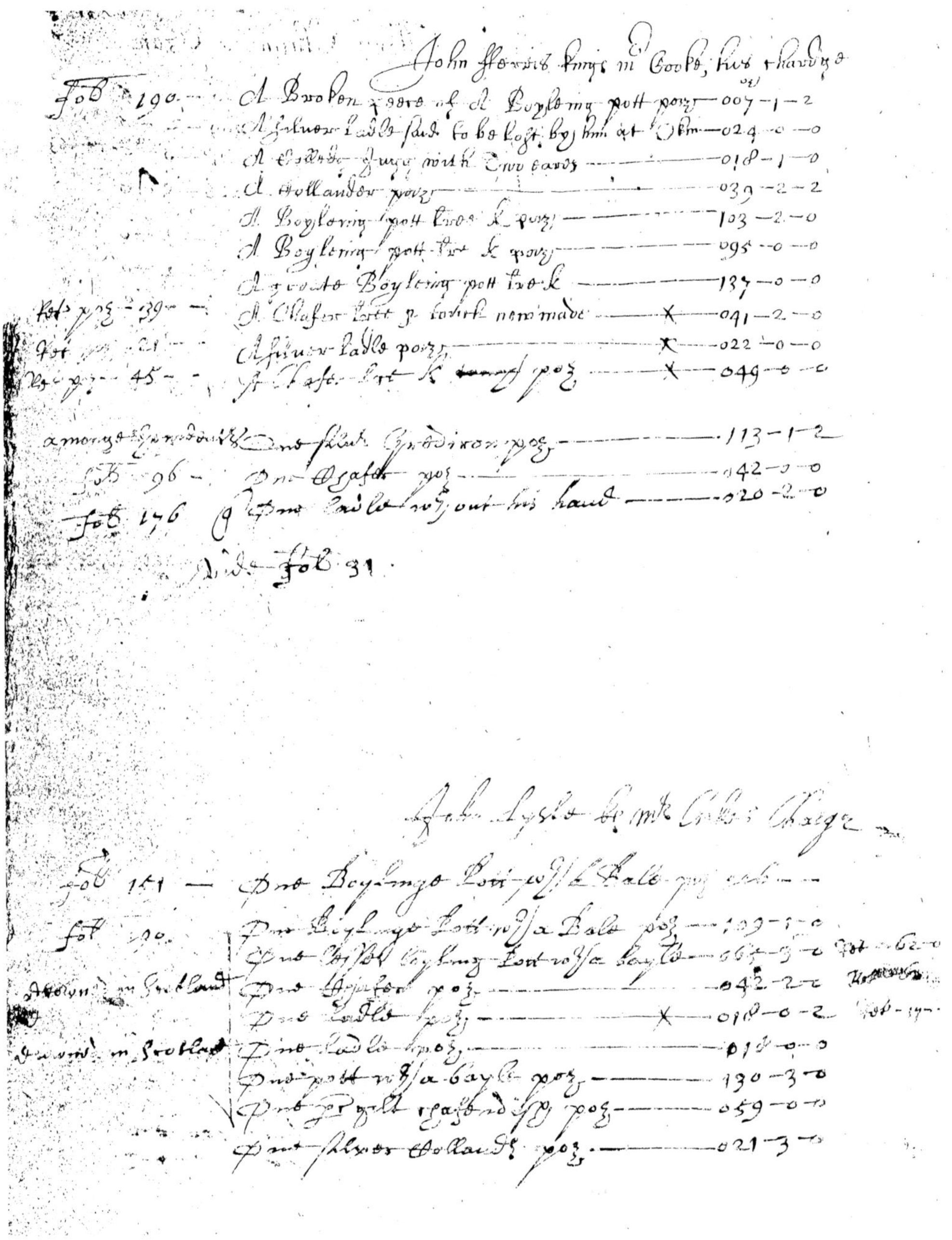

John Flowers Kings m[aste]r Cooke his charge

Fol 190 — A Broken cover of a Boyling pott poiz — 007 - 1 - 2
A silver ladle said to be kept by him at [illegible] — 024 - 0 - 0
A [illegible] Jugg with two eares — 018 - 1 - 0
A Hollander poiz — 039 - 2 - 2
A Boyling pott two e[ares] poiz — 103 - 2 - 0
A Boyling pott two e[ares] poiz — 095 - 0 - 0
A greate Boyling pott two e[ares] — 137 - 0 - 0
[illegible] — A Chafer [illegible] new made — 041 - 2 - 0
[illegible] — A silver ladle poiz — 022 - 0 - 0
[illegible] 45 — A Chafer [illegible] poiz — 049 - 0 - 0

amongst [illegible] — One silver Gridiron poiz — 113 - 1 - 2
Fol 96 — One Chafer poiz — 042 - 0 - 0
Fol 176 — One ladle w[i]th out his hand — 020 - 2 - 0

Vide Fol 31

[illegible] Charge

Fol 151 — One Boylinge Pott w[i]th a Bale poiz [illegible]
Fol 190 — One Boylinge Pott w[i]th a Bale poiz — 109 - [illegible] - 0
One [illegible] Boyling Pott w[i]th a bayle — 065 - 3 - 0
[illegible] in Scotland — One Chafer poiz — 042 - 2 - 0
One ladle poiz — 018 - 0 - 2
[illegible] in Scotland — One ladle poiz — 018 - 0 - 0
One pott w[i]th a bayle poiz — 130 - 3 - 0
One [illegible] poiz — 059 - 0 - 0
One silver Hollander poiz — 021 - 3 - 0

Burntisland 'til 1633

The events of July 1633 were but one small incident in the Royal Burgh of Burntisland's long history. Its location sheltered within a bay has meant its use by man since prehistory, when Mesolithic hunter-gatherers ranged along the coastline of Eastern Scotland. It may already have been a settlement, inhabited by the Picts, when the Roman Legions, during the reign of the Emperor Antoninus Pius, arrived. From about A.D. 143 they built a turf defensive wall across Scotland at its narrowest point. Antonine's wall was occupied for about fifty years and during that time the Legions forayed north into Fife and beyond. Its safe anchorage may have afforded an excellent site for the Romans to exploit in their military excursions into Fife. The Romans, however, were but a brief interlude in the life of the village that would become Burntisland. The Picts united with other tribes and by A.D. 900 had become a nation, a nation of Scots able to stand together against the next invader, who came not from the south but from the far north. The Vikings, who had first appeared when the Picts and the Scots were still struggling for supremacy, raiding into the Firth of Forth, clashed with both Pictish armies and navies. Sometimes victory was theirs and at other times the Picts but eventually the united tribes forced them to the west of Scotland and Burntisland suffered no longer from the "Scourge of the Seas." Scotland prospered and with it, Burntisland. A castle, now called Rossend, built by the Abbey of Dunfermline was erected in the 12th century. It suggests the importance of the site, not only as a safe haven, but also as a ferry crossing point. Viking raids had faded from memory when King Alexander fell from his horse a little to the East of the village in the year 1286; a fatal accident that fanned the flames of rebellion and counter rebellion which plagued Scotland for the next hundred years. Burntisland was little heard of through those turbulent times and it is not until the 16th century that it reappears with any vigour. The house of Stewart had ruled Scotland for over 200 years when James granted the town a charter in 1541 with the purpose of developing the harbour as a naval base. A year later he was dead and his infant daughter proclaimed queen.

The reign of Mary Queen of Scots is closely linked with Fife and it is not surprising that Burntisland also had its parts to play in the tragic drama. In 1563 Mary stayed at Burntisland Castle, overnight, enroute to St. Andrews. An unofficial member of her court was the French poet Pierre de Chastelard, who had already been admonished, having been discovered in her bedchamber in Holyrood Palace. That night he was again discovered in Mary's private chambers. This final indiscretion resulted in Pierre being taken to St. Andrews and executed. At the Market Cross in St. Andrews he is said to have shouted,
"Adieu, thou most beautiful and most cruel Princess in the world".

Mary ended her life far from the Forth though she still lived when her son, James VI, granted Royal Burgh status to Burntisland. The year was 1586 and Burntisland was growing, growing with the increasing trade with Europe, the Low Countries in particular. James VI's involvement continued and he stayed at Burntisland Castle in 1601. As the result of a riding accident which befell James VI, the General Assembly of the Church, which was to have been held at St. Andrews, was transferred to the Parish church in Burntisland. The church had been completed as recently as 1595. This was James' final (and only) royal visit to Scotland after the Union of the Crowns in 1603. The coronation journey of Charles I is modelled on that journey which took place sixteen years before in the summer of 1617. The running of the town was in the hands of the Town Council;[22] a group of leading citizens of which Captain Andrew Watson[23], being Master of the Prime Guild, was prominent. Their duties were myriad and the beginnings of the seventeenth century were eventful for trading burghs like Burntisland[24]. The Thirty Years War, which Charles had entered on the European mainland, brought opportunities to men like Captain Watson[25] but also responsibilities and costs to the coastal burghs[26]. The financial burden on the coastal towns was already being felt before Charles's visit of 1633[27] and the extra effort needed may not have been welcome[28].
I add a list culled from the sources of the inhabitants of Burntisland[29].

Coronation Journey

James the Sixth (First of England) died in 1625. However, while his eldest surviving son, Charles, was crowned King of England almost immediately in London, Parliament in Edinburgh insisted that he be crowned King of Scotland in Scotland's capital, Edinburgh. After some wrangling a date was finally scheduled for the Coronation ceremony: June 18th, 1633.

The entire journey and celebrations were closely modelled on the visit of James VI in 1617. A great deal of money was expended in improving and decorating the Royal route[30]. The Privy Council had set up a commission some time before to report on the state of the roads and to carry out the necessary work to improve the whole route[31]. Sir James Balfour, Lord Lyon of Scotland at the time, who, in fact, organised and devised the schedule of the coronation itself, has left us an account[32]. The King left London on May 10th along with a vast train of nobles, courtiers, guards, servants, etc[33]. The journey up the East Coast was attended by continuous spectacle. At each day's stops the local noble would lay on a masque or other entertainment[34]. The King and his closest retainers would be housed in the noble's castle while the lesser members of the train would be put up in ever-decreasing levels of comfort, dependent on status. Resting four nights at Berwick the Royal train passed into Scotland on June 12th arriving in Edinburgh on the 15th [35]. On the eve of the coronation Charles made a procession from his palace, Holyrood House, to the Castle. A great state banquet was held seating over two hundred guests; the majority of the cutlery and dinner services used having been brought up from London in the train itself or by boat[36]. The next day he again made procession down the Royal Mile. Unlike the day before, when he arrived in a great coach[37], again brought up from London, this time he was mounted on his great charger[38].

The coronation, in the Abbey beside Holyrood House, was something of a shock to the Puritan Scots. The elaborate ritual raised suspicion of a return to Catholicism among many. The journey and subsequent coronation of Charles I is much too great a story to do justice to here. For the purposes of this volume we are more concerned with the logistics of the operation; in particular the transport arrangements and some other detail that touch upon the plot. The ability to move a monarch and his court around his realm was a highly developed art by the 17th century. All aspects, from transport to provisions, had to be considered as well as the need for effective communication in order to keep both foreign and domestic policy working. Accommodation was needed for the immediate Court, their servants and their servants. The party that travelled with King Charles was considerable. I will allow the reader to compute the final figures of men and horses. The detail that still survives for this journey is great. Orders, lists and instructions were issued for everything needed for the journey[39]. These include the mention of carts from the Tower of London. The attention to detail was all embracing, from organising an effective postal service to sending someone over to France for supplies of wine. The Court in London was responsible for the "luxury items" brought with it (dinner services etc.[40]) while the Council in Edinburgh took responsibility for accommodation[41] and victualling[42] requirements for the Royal train. It is in the Scottish instructions that we find James Clark and Robert Kilgour among the many men responsible for the supply of horses for transportation. The instructions for the conveyance of the baggage train is interesting in that it represents an early rateable value for the various parishes[43], each parish having to supply so many horses dependent on the number of ploughs that the locality supported. Each plough would need a number of teams to operate it so the request for a single team for each plough may represent a tax of 25%.

Parliament 1633

The Scottish parliament called in June 1633 was the first since Charles's father James VI had met the Estates in 1617. The religious issues that had been so problematic at that parliament had not been resolved. Rather they had been allowed to fester with the result that some of the difficulties that Charles faced were a direct result of his father's insistence of the adoption of the Five Articles[44]. Following the coronation, the Scottish Parliament met and again, the sessions caused disquiet, this time due to the King's autocratic style and his unwillingness to listen to argument. When it came time to vote on the Acts put forward, the King was seen to be noting the names of the 'No' voters on a sheet of paper and threatened the Earl of Rothes with prosecution for treason when the earl disputed the count[45]. Matters were not helped by the appointment of Sir John Hay as Clerk register as he had already caused disquiet in Scotland over the handling of a scheme for the Sea fishing industry[46]. It should be pointed out that the accounts included were written after the event and by writers who had a particular message to convey. But there is general consensus that it was amidst some bad feeling[47] that the parliamentary sessions were concluded and Charles embarked on a tour of Royal Palaces. Charles, accompanied by the entourage that had travelled with him from London, stayed one night at Linlithgow, two nights at Stirling; thence to his birthplace, Dunfermline, where they stayed one night and then to the Royal Hunting Palace of Falkland for a five night stay. However, in order to show his friends 'real highlanders', a one day and night excursion had been hastily organised, whilst in Edinburgh, to Perth.

Aftermath

Attitudes to Scotland in England had been coloured ever since James VI had gone South in 1603 to take the Crown. He took with him a large number of Scotsmen who proceeded to accept most of the positions of power, much to the chagrin of the English court. Though not in the same numbers, by 1633, there were still a large number of Scots in Charles Court. The majority had made London their permanent abode and rarely visited North. Compared to the refinement of the Court at Whitehall and the cosmopolitan nature of London itself, Scotland, even Edinburgh, would have appeared very backward and poverty stricken (which, to a large extent, it was). The two extracts, one actually about the visit of James VI/I[48], serve to illustrate the alienation felt by visiting courtiers. The second extract from the court diarist[49] is more telling. I only extract a few lines at the end of the page which concerns Edinburgh but I believe it carries on the theme of the first extract regarding the alien aspect to the eyes of a southerner. The diary itself peters out at the Stirling entry, revealing, I suggest, a less than professional interest in further proceedings! The original plan for the progress had included, after returning to Edinburgh, a five-night stay with some day trips. However, evidence shows that Charles had already decided to return to London earlier[50]. A number of factors, political, religious and personal, contributed to making the decision by the 28th June. (though it is interesting to read the Venetian ambassador's view of the visit[51]). It is possible an 'official' version had been carefully constructed for consumption by foreign diplomats like the Venetian ambassador. Letters ordering coaches and horses for the earlier date were sent from Edinburgh[52]. So the King was probably thinking of Whitehall, Greenwich Palace and his beloved Henrietta[53] as he rose at 9 o'clock that wet Wednesday morning in July 1633. He was only to visit one more time, under very different circumstances. The events that started in Scotland in 1633 ended for Charles at Whitehall in January 1649 when he was beheaded by the government of the day.

One final extract from the records[54] gives us the name of the criminal, Robert Tough. Whether he was ever in Burntisland, I can't say for certain but the idea of of a wanted criminal on the run during a royal visit (not to mention the idea of an illicit love affair) appealed to the romantic in me. And I liked his name.

POSTSCRIPT.   Another Tragedy

Introduction

The fear of witchcraft was real in the 17th Century. Charles' father James VI/I was particularly concerned and a number of witch trials took place during his reign. Two are of interest. The first took place while James was still King of Scotland. A number of women in Berwick were tried as witches. Among the charges brought was one of raising storms. The other is the 1612 trial of the Lancashire witches of Pendle Forest. Two families were accused of witchcraft; the Sowtherns and the Whittles. Women, known as Old Demdike and Old Chattox headed both families. Old Demdike implicated her daughter Elizabeth Device and two of her grandchildren, James and Alison Device. Old Chattox and Alison Device were imprisoned in Lancaster Castle.

The case developed when a plot was revealed to rescue them by blowing up the castle. James Device testified that about 20 people, all of them alleged to be witches, had met at his mother's farmhouse of Malking Tower. The majority was arrested. At the final trial, nine year old Jennet, the second daughter of Elizabeth Device, testified against the whole family. Jennet stated that she had often seen a spirit visit her mother in the form of a brown dog, which she called Ball. The spirit would ask her mother what it was required to do and she would name the person she wanted killed. Twelve of the accused were hung. Old Demdike and Old Chattox admitted they were witches, but the rest declared their innocence until the end.

The following letters are an 'echo' of the 1612 case. They concern us as one of the charges leveled against the accused was of raising a storm on the afternoon of 10th July 1633. The reader will note that Jennet Device, now a thirty-year-old woman and Malking Tower are included in the 'plot'. The charges were ultimately dropped and father and son Robinson committed to prison as cheats and imposters.

May 16th. 1634   Brocklesby

Sir William Pelham to Edward Viscount Conway and Killultagh

……..The greatest news from the country is of a huge pack of witches which are lately discovered in Lancashire, whereof it is said 19 are condemned, and that there are at least 60 already discovered, and yet daily there are more revealed; there are divers of them of good ability and they have done much harm. It is suspected that they had a hand in raising the great storm wherein his Majesty was in so great danger at sea in Scotland………

June 15th 1634

Bishop Bridgman, of Chester, to Secs. Coke and Windebank.

Received order to examine seven of the persons condemned for witches in Lancaster. John Spencer, Alice Higgin, and Jennet Loynd, died lately in gaol, and Jennet Hargrave, laid sick past hope of recovery. The other three the Bishop had examined and inclosed their examinations. The old woman, Margaret Johnson, alias the penitent witch, with tears in her eyes, after an exhortation by the Bishop, replied,

"I will not add sin to sin, I have already done enough, nay too much, and I will not increase it. I pray God I may repent."

And then she confessed as is set down in her examination, often acknowledging that she was a witch, but more often faulting in the particulars of her actions, as one having a strong imagination of the former, but of too weak a memory to retain or relate the other. The others whom he examined their wisdoms will soon discover guilt or innocence. Conceit and malice are so powerful with many in those parts, that they will easily afford an oath to work revenge upon their neighbour, and it was offered to be deposed by Mary Fisher, widow, (where the parties dieted in the assizes week,) that if Dicconson would have given the accuser Robinson 40s. before the arraignment, neither he nor his son (the boy that first set the business on foot) would have said anything against her; but when she advised her husband to give nothing, Robinson said he had no malice to any but her. The like will be testified by others, but such evidence being, as lawyers speak, against the King, the Bishop thought it not meet without further authority to examine. (seal with arms.)   Inclosed,

Separate examinations of Margaret Johnson, Mary Spencer, and Frances Dicconson, taken at Lancaster
13th June, 1634, by Bishop Bridgman of Chester.

MARGARET JOHNSON, widow, aged 60, being examined, says she has been a witch about six years; was brought thereto upon some vexations of her bad neighbours. About that time, walking in the highway in Marsden in Whalley, there appeared to her a man in black attire, with black points, who said to her, if she would give him her soul, she would want nothing, but she would have power to hurt whom she would. She refused and he vanished. In this manner he ofttimes resorted to her, till at last she yielded, and he gave into her hand gold and silver; but it vanished soon again, and she was ever bare and poor, though he oft gave her the like. He called himself Mamilion, and most commonly at his coming had the use of her body; after this he appeared in the shape of a brown coloured dog, a white cat, and a hare, and in these shapes sucked her blood in a manner described. She never hurt man or woman by witchcraft, only Henry Heap her neighbour called her a witch before she was one, whereupon her spirit willed her to hurt him, but she assented not; yet (forgetting herself) she said Heap was dead ere her spirit advised her to it. There were seven or eight of her neighbours who were witches, but most of them
are dead. Jane, wife of Roger Cartmell of Colne, is the only one she can name. Since her imprisonment her familiar never came near her. The rest of the witches now in gaol were unknown to her; is persuaded that Wilkinson and his wife are not witches, because he daily prays and reads and seems a godly man. She frequented the church till her compact with the devil, but seldom since.

MARY SPENCER, of Burnley, aged 20, being examined, utterly denies that she knows any witchcraft, never did hurt to anybody thereby. Prays God to forgive Nicholas Cunliffe, who having borne malice to her and her parents these 5 or 6 years, has lately wrongfully abused them. Her father and mother were condemned last assizes for witches, and are since dead and buried. Before her imprisonment usually went to church at Burnley and heard Mr. Brierley, and what she could remember used to repeat to her parents at home. Repeated the Creed and Lords Prayer, and says she defies the devil and all his works, and hopes to be saved by Christ Jesus. Cunliffe accused her to call a collock, or pail, which came running to her of its own accord. When she was arraigned she would have answered for herself, but the wind was so loud and the throng so great that she could not hear the evidence against her. When she was a young girl and went to the well for water, she used to tumble or trundle the collock, or peal, down the hill, and she would run along after it to overtake it, and did overhie it sometimes, and then might call it to come to her, but utterly denies that she could ever make it come to her by any witchcraft. She is not afraid of death, for she hopes it will make an entrance for her into heaven.

FRANCES DICCONSON, wife of John Dicconson, husbandman in Pendle Forest in Whalley, being examined denies all knowledge of witchcraft. The boy who accused her has much wronged her. His father, Edmund Rough, alias Robinson, bought a cow of her husband, but he would not let her go without surety, whereupon he has since maliced her and her husband. The other witness against her, Edmund Stevenson, of Stainskow in Pendle, is lately accused of felony, and maliced her upon bargain of

butter, but formerly in the audience of John Nutter, steward of Blackburn hundred, and John Hargraves of Higham, and John Radcliffe of the Highhouses in Whalley, confessed he knew nothing of her but well. Edmund Robinson offered to have freed her if her husband would have given 40s., and for that end dealt with Richard Hooker of Pendle Forest.

June 29th 1634 Whitehall.

The Council to Alexander Baker and Sergeant William Clowes, his Majesty's surgeons.

They are to make choice of midwives to inspect and search the bodies of those women lately brought up by the Sheriff of co. Lancaster indicted for witchcraft, wherein the midwives are to receive instructions from Dr. Harvey, the King's physician and themselves. (Indorsed, "The prisoners are at the Ship Tavern at Greenwich")

July 2nd 1634   Surgeon's Hall, Mugwell Street, London.

Certificate of William Clowes, Alexander Baker, and five other Surgeons, and of ten certified midwives,
to the Council.

Under directions of Dr. Harvey, and in his presence, they have inspected the women lately brought up from Lancaster, and find on the bodies of Janet Hargraves, Frances Dicconson, and Mary Spencer nothing unnatural nor anything like a teat or mark. On the body of Margaret Johnson they find two things which may be called teats, the first.....

July 10th 1634

Examination of Edmund Robinson the younger, of Newchurch, co. Lancaster, aged ten years or thereabouts, taken by George Long, Justice of the Peace for Middlesex, by command of Sec. Windebank.

Examinant told his father and mother, and the Justices of the Peace, and Judges of Assize of co. Lancaster, and divers other persons, of divers things concerning the finding two greyhounds and starting a hare, and that the greyhounds refused to run at the hare, and that he tied the greyhounds to a bush and beat them, and that thereupon one assumed the shape of a woman, and the other of a boy, and that the woman offered the examinant twelvepence to say nothing, and that she put a bridle into the boy's mouth, whereupon he became a white horse, and took up examinant, and carried him on his back to a place called Horestones in Pendle Forest, where he saw a number of persons gathered together who gave examinant meat , etc. He now say, that all that tale is false and feigned, and has no truth at all, but only as he has heard tales and reports made by women, so he framed his tale out of his own invention, which when he had once told he still persisted in, until he came to the King's coachman at Richmond, to whom he declared the truth. He invented the said tale for that his mother having brought him up to spin wool, and also used him to fetch home her kine, he was appointed one time to fetch home her kine but did not do it, but went to play with other children, and fearing his father or mother would beat him, he made this tale for an excuse. Denies that he ever saw any boy with a cloven foot, or any woman called Loynd wife in a wood as though she had first been a lantern and after a woman, but told these tales to excuse himself when he had been at play.

July 16th 1634

Petition of Edmund Robinson, a poor distressed prisoner in the Gatehouse, to Sec. Windebank.

Has been imprisoned since the 28th June in great want, having neither money nor friends, and being almost 200 miles from his poor house. Is ignorant of the cause of his imprisonment, but is informed that it is by reason of a petition against him by Mr. Duxbury, one of the jury, when the prisoners that are condemned for witchcraft were found guilty. Petitioner never gave evidence against them, nor prosecuted them. He has been told that Duxbury has received money from John Dicconson to prosecute the business for his wife. What he alleges against the petitioner is only for his own benefit, and to gain money. Petitioner prays that he may appear and answer before Windebank to what Duxbury shall object, and that order may be given for his releasement.

July 16th 1634

Re-examination of Edmund Robinson the younger, taken before George Long.
Being examined touching his accusation of Frances, wife of John Dicconson, Jennet, wife of Henry Hargraves, Jennet Devys, William Devys, her half brother, and ? Beawse, to be witches, and that they were at a witch feast at Horestones in Pendle Forest, he says that he had heard the neighbours talk of a witch feast that was kept at Malking Tower in Pendle Forest about twenty years since, to which feast divers witches came, and many were apprehended and executed at Lancaster, and thereupon he framed those tales concerning the persons aforesaid, because he heard the neighbours repute them for witches. He heard Edmund Stevenson say that he was much troubled with the said Dicconson's wife in the time of his sickness, and that he suspected her, and he heard Robert Smith say that his wife, lying upon her death bed, accused Jennet Hargraves to be the cause of her death.; and he heard William Nutter's wife say that Jennet Devys and William Devys had bewitched her; and it was generally spoken that Beawse's wife, who went a-begging, was witch, and he had heard Sharpee Smith say that the wife of John Loynd laid her hand upon a cow of his, after which she never rose.

47

FOOTNOTES

HISTORICAL REFERENCES.

FOOTNOTES

1. Annals of Scotland J Balfour. (1600 - 1657)

The 10th of July being Wednesday, his majesty early removed from Falkland to Edinburgh, where his passage from Burntisland to Leith, he was in great jeopardy of his life by a sudden storm which did arise after a great rain that had been all the preceding night and morning, but spent itself in less than half an hour. His majesty with no small danger recovered his own ship, which waited for him in Burnt island Road, later landing from it at Leith, only there was a little boat with some of the king's plate and money's, and 8 servants lost.

2. Historie of the Kirk of Scotland 1568 - 1646). Row. (1558 - 1637)

  : And returning to Edinburgh out of Falkland, he came to Burntisland, and past over to Leith in a pinnace of his own; but the day being somewhat tempestuous, many going over the water at that time , a little boat, wherein there were sundry Englishmen, the King's servants, and rich coffers, were drowned in sight of the King's pinnace, which made the King melancholy that night.

3. Troubles 1624 - 1645   Annals   Spalding. (c. 1609 - 1670)

The king ……., and came back to Burntisland, shipped, came over the water, and safely lodged in the Abbey (Holyrood) that night. But, as he is on the water, in his own sight, their perished a boat following after him, having within her about 35 persons, of English and Scots, his own domestic servants, and only two escaped with their lives. His majesty's silver plate and household stuff perished with the rest.

4. Diary. William Laud. Bishop of London. (1573 - 1645)

Wednesday 10th July

His Majesties dangerous passage from Burntisland to Edinburgh.

5. State Papers (Domestic)

July 11th Edinburgh. Sec. Coke to Sec. Windebank

  ….. Yesterday, in passing the sea from Falkland, a boat was cast away and some people and goods lost; but the King and all the Lords are in safety and good health. Tomorrow they turn their faces towards Windebank. …… (endorsed by Windebank, "Rec, 16, in the morning.")

6. State Papers (Domestic)

July 14th Seaton. Edward Viscount Conway and Killultagh to William Weld.

…… Weld would shortly hear of the King's * * * and the danger he escaped (in crossing) the Forth.

7. Traquair House
Extract from replies to burghs's objections to May Island Lighthouse Committee 1636

Replies to the forgoing objections on behalf of the burghs, in regard to sea ferries. Maintains first, generally that there are abuses, that acts and ordinances for sufficient provision of boats, etc. are not observed. That loss has been caused and danger of life by ferry boats not carrying bridges, which were only carried by the boats in Leith , and no where else. That if no complaints had been made it is because of the trouble attendant thereon. That the boatmen especially between Leith and Burntisland were unruly. That they collected fares a mile or two out at sea and compelled passengers to pay double under pain of detention. They did this when it was calm under pretext of the hard work required in rowing, and when it was stormy they demanded double fares for the risk run. Abuses and exaction between Leith and Fife - (2) The casting away in 1633 of above 50 of his Majesty's domestics with
100,000 l. in goods, through negligence.

8. Register of the Privy Council (Scotland)

Acta Feb. 1628 - July 1629. Fol. 69,b.

attending - Praeses?; Winton; Linlithgow; Buccleuch; Galloway; Bishop of Dunblane; Master of Elpinstone; Master of Jedburgh; Secretary; Clerk of Register; Advocate; Sir John Scot.

Holyrood House, 11th December 1628

Concerning the supplication presented to the Lords of Secret Council by the Provost and Baillies of Edinburgh making mention that when our late Sovereign lord came to this kingdom they built a bark for his Majesty's transport between the ferries, and it was our sovereign now present his pleasure that they should do like against his Majesty's herecoming, which in all submissive and dutiful obedience the said supplicants are willing to perform, but they are informed that there is some other course intended for his Majesty's service in this point whereunto (if so be his Majesty's pleasure) they are willing in all humility to acquiesce, humbly desiring therefore the said Lords to let them know how to carry themselves in this matter, , like as at more length is contained in the said supplication. Whereupon Alexander, Earl of Linlithgow, High Admiral of this kingdom, being heard, and he being demanded if he had any purpose or intention to do anything in this matter, he declared that the charge of that business belonged unto him as his Majesty's Admiral, and that he would do therein that which to the duty and credit of his place and charge appertained for his Majesty's honour and contentment.

In respect of the declaration made by the Lord High Admiral the Lords of Secret Council exonerate and relieve the said supplicants of all blame, crime and imputation that may be imputed against them or laid to there charge for not preparing of a bark for his Majesty's transport between the ferries and declares them to be freed and exonerated thereof for ever.

9. Register of the Privy Council (Scotland)

March 5th 1629.

The Lords of Secret Council, remembering that the Magistrates of the burgh of Edinburgh made offer to prepare a pinnace upon their own charges, for transporting of his Majesty to and from Leith, Burntisland and Kinghorn; and that the Earl of Linlithgow, Lord Admiral opposed the same, and undertook the burden thereof as a point proper to his charge; Therefore the Lords find, that if his Majesty's Admiral has or will build a pinnace for that service, that he must do it upon his own charges, and that his Majesty's coffers must not be burdened therewith.

10. Register of the Privy Council (Scotland)

sheet of paper - minutes
….Regarding the ferryboats.………

sheet of paper - Minutes to be done before the Kings homecoming.
…To speak with the Admiral about the ships and ferryboats. ….

sheet of paper listing things to be done. (Privy Council Committee ?)
Item - that some sail canvas be provided for covering of the carts at the time of remove.…

11. Burntisland Burgh Records Tuesday 9th July 1633

Convenit Burntisland Counsel. Understanding that the King his majesty is to visit …….
Ordaineth two boats to be provided for him and noblemen who should happen to go with him. And the said boats to be equipped by **Capt. A Watson** by **John Smith**, John Boswell, James Shaw, Robert Whyte, **David Murray**, Henry Henryson, John Mason, **James Watt elder** and Robert Brown ferrier and a boat to be equipped by **Capt. J Orrock** by, **William Brown, Robert Harroware, James Wat younger, James Common, Robert Williamson, John Gordoun, Robert Wilson and Robert Ennand**.

Ordaineth to be ready in the harbour and await upon Andrew Watson…. Attend upon high matters.

12. Statistical Account of Scotland

The harbour certainly is one of the best in Scotland. By way of excellence it is called, in some of the town's charters, "Portus Gratiae" and "Portus Salutis" It is here that ships generally take shelter, when driven up by storms, and hard gales of easterly wind. It is easily entered, and affords the greatest safety, let the wind blow from any quarter. It is very capacious, and of great depth of water. Much improvement might still be made upon it. Were the quays extended, small ships could come in, and go out, at any time of tide. ……… There is another thing respecting this harbour, which deserves to be pointed out to government, and may at least merit their consideration. It is this; that it might be made one of the safest and most convenient watering place possible for his Majesty's ships in the firth. At no great expense, a run of the finest water might be introduced by a pipe, and carried to any of the quays thought most proper, where the king's boats might receive it, without the least trouble or danger. This may be thought the more worthy of notice, as, it is well known, that the present mode of watering the king's ships, either by going to Leith, or Starly - burn, a place on the north shore, about a mile to the westward of Burntisland, is often attended with danger, and sometimes with loss.

There are at present three large stout boats, and a small one that goes at the half tide. They cross every day when passengers appear.
The shore for a quarter mile eastward, is all sandy, till it joins the Pettycur harbour, near Kinghorn.
Opposite the sandy beach, the sea has made great encroachments within these hundred years, and still continues to gain ground. Near the town, however, the rocks are a perfect defence.

13. Computer program SHM19 (V. 11/88)

Tide times for Burntisland 10th July 1633.
High : 0500 hr. / 1700 hr. Low : 1100 hr. / 2300 hr.

14. Burntisland Records   3rd August 1633

Body of **John Ferries**, the King's cook washed ashore. On the body was found

" £45 in dollars and other white money, 5 twelve pound pieces in gold, ane single angel, in all £107 5s 4d; gold ring, rapier belt and hanger. Item a coat and breeches of camblet"

The Baillies think that the sums bestowed on his burial be paid to the following persons ;
To Andro Orrock for making his graif, 16 shillings
Item to John White for ringing the bell, 16 shillings
Item to **Janet Mair** and **Elspat Coasin** for winding him, 13 shillings

Item to William Mitchel for washing his cot and breeks, 16 shillings

Item to James Brown tayleour for 5 elms of linen to be his winding sheet, five pund 8 shillings

Item to David Stirling for making his kist, 3 lib 10 shillings

Item to warkmen for carrying him to the Tolbuith, 32 shillings

Item to Alexander Barnie for first spying him in ye wold, 31 shillings

Item ane dollar to pay for the winding sheet of the other man found with him.

Sept 17th.

Lord High Admiral (Earl of Linlithgow) anchors in Burntisland Roads and

' desired the money and other effects to be given up to him.'

Dec. 14th

Council retained property

' deducting always £40 to be given to the Lord Admiral for his good will.'

Balance of £51 and effects handed to the Kirk Session

' the Council think it expedient that the Session build a seat round the pulpit for such aged men as cannot well hear the minister's voice.'

15. Traquair House

A note of what the clothes **Mr. Andrew Troughton**, one of his majesties servants of the silver scullery,

had on when he was cast away in Scotland,

the 10th July 1633 / viz.

An horseman's coat of whitish colour cloth with silk and silver buttons.

His doublet and hose of cloth near white colour, of his coat the doublet had hard buttons

and the hose worn pared longer at the top, about a length or something more with a little darker coloured cloth.

For his height he was of middling height, the hair of his head was black and the hair of
his beard a light brown.

50 or 60 pounds in money that he had about him when he was castaway.

16. Tower of London Jewel House Records. Mildmay Papers Somerset Record Office

John Ferris. Mr. Cook his charges now upon him at his death and all discharged.

10th July	impressed and silvered gridiron	113 - 1 - 2
fol. 96	one chaser. drowned in Scotland	42 - 0 - 0
fol. 176	one ladle	20 - 2 - 0
fol. 13	a broken spout of a boiling pot	7 - 1 - 2
	a ladle lost at Okm.	24 - 0 - 0
	a chaser. drowned in Scotland	57 - 3 - 2

17. Tower of London Jewel House Records.   Mildmay Papers S.R.O.
John Lysle by Mr. Cookes charge

fol. 151	one boiling pot with a Bale x oz	116 - 0 - 0
fol. 190	| one boiling pot with a Bale x oz	109 – 1 - 0
	| one copper boiling pot with a ladle	65 – 3 - 0
drowned in Scotland	| one server? x oz	42 – 2 - 0
	| one ladle x oz	18 - 0 - 2
drowned in Scotland	| one ladle x oz	18 - 0 - 0
	| one pot with a bayle x oz	130 - 3 - 0
	| one pair gilt chason? Dishes x oz	59 - 0 - 0
	| one ? colander x oz	21 - 3 - 0

18. Tower of London Jewel House Records.   Mildmay Papers S.R.O.

Listed as dead 1634.
Name.   Title.   Department.
Francis Husthwaite Sergeant Pantry Cuthbert Joyner Sergeant Pastry Hugh Roberts Yeoman
Cellar James Bohannay Yeoman Buttery Richard Cholmoly Yeoman Buttery Daniel Clarke
Master Cook   William Calvorley Yeoman Pantry

19. Tower of London Jewel House Records. Mildmay Papers Somerset Records Office.

10th April 1634 The Sergeant of the Scullery his new charge at this day.

16 Chargers	16 chargers
16 platters	40 plates
20 deep plates	38 deep plates Arms Engraved
32 dishes Arms Stamped.	18 dishes
16 deep dishes	18 deep dishes
24 small dishes	
28 salad dishes	
1 small dish	Total 283 dishes.

20. Papers of the Privy Council (Domestic)

August 1633

Note of such carts as were used into Scotland and are not yet returned back. (abridged)

Use.	Signed out to.	Number.
The Wardrobe	Mr. Bishop	3 carts
The equerries	Mr. John Houghton	1 cart
The Kitchens	**Jasper Lynsey Wm. Atkinson.**	3 carts
Secretary Coke	Henry Millington	1 cart
Confectionary	George Shamlbury	1 cart
Privy Chamber	Mr. Adrian May	1 cart
Earl of Carlisle	Robinson	1 cart
Robes	Robert Josley	1 cart
Master of the Horse	John ?	1 cart

21. Papers of the Privy Council (Domestic)

Oct. 18th. Notes of Sec. Windebank of Council business undispatched.

......return of carts borrowed for the journey into Scotland.

22. Statistical Account Vol. II No. 38.

Entry for Burntisland.

The government of it is vested in twenty - one persons, of whom fourteen are termed guild councilors, consisting of merchants, tradesmen, skippers, seamen, and land labourers; of whom three are chosen yearly at Michaelmas, by the old and new council, to be bailies; the other seven are trade - councilors, being one of each trade. There is also a provost chosen yearly at Michaelmas. If he is a nobleman, he is a supernumerary; but if a burgher, he is included in the above number.

23. Protocol Books Burntisland.

Documentary History of Mary Somerville's House P.C.A.S. 1957

6th June 1628 - Sasine **Captain Andrew Watson** and **Isobell Boswell** his spouse on resignation by John   Watson jnr. Heir of John Watson burgess in Burntisland.

16th August 1653 - Sasine **John Watson** as heir to his father Captain Andrew Watson.

Property to the west owned by Robert Angus and to the east by John Cairns alias Walker.

24. Burntisland. Early History. J. Blyth 1948.

In January, 1620, the Privy Council recommended to all Churches in Scotland and to the Magistrates of all the burghs the case of Robert Cowan, master of the ship " William" of Burntisland, who, in September, 1619, embarked a cargo of pilchards in Ireland and sailed for Alicante, in Spain. Cowan had reached a point " about the South Cap" on 25th September when he was boarded by a suprise attack in the half light of dawn, his assailant being a Turkish carvell of six pieces of ordnance. The William and her crew were taken to Tittiwane, on the

Barbary Coast, where the master and six seamen were sold as slaves to the moors the ship herself being afterwards sold at Algiers. The prisoners were put to arduous work in a mill and very badly fed, their rations being mainly composed of dusty bread with a scanty allowance of water. They were worked from dawn till dusk, and housed at night in an underground place without a vestige of bedding. Two Burntisland shipmasters, John Dury and Robert Richardson, were appointed as collectors of the fund for the captives release.

25. Privy Council (Scotland)

April 20th 1626. Letter of Marque - to **Andrew Watson**, captain of the Burntisland ship called 'The Blessing', empowering him to go to sea with arms and artillery and to attack and capture all Spanish ships, or ships of the Spanish Netherlands, or of other dominions of Spain, and to arrest all ships of other nations going to Spanish ports with arms or provisions.

26. Privy Council (Scotland)

July 11th 1626. Receipt of a letter from his Majesty, dated 1st July, intimating that, as he is credibly informed that there is great preparation of forces for a Spanish invasion of Britain, he is fitting out two fleets …………. In these circumstances and the rather because he is also informed that the intentions of the Spaniards are immediately against Scotland, " where they presume a party," he requires the Council to take order for the security of the Scottish coasts, and moreover to levy 500 able Scottish mariners, or as many as can be spared, and send them to Newcastle, to be drafted thence into one or other of the two English fleets.   Resolution by the Council, in consequence, that, as this demand of his Majesty requires the concurrence and assistance of the burghs, missives be sent to twenty of the burghs, - viz. Edinburgh, Dundee, Aberdeen, Glasgow, Ayr, Montrose, St. Andrews, Crail, Anstruther Easter, Anstruther Wester, Pittenweem, Dysart, Kirkcaldy, Kinghorn, Burntisland, Irvine, Dumbarton, Preston, Wemyss and Borrowstounness, - ordering them to send Commissioners with instructions on the subject to meet the Council on the 25th next.

27. Privy Council (Scotland)

July 25th, - Commissioners from the twenty burghs attend the Council as had been ordered, and report the utter inability of the country to furnish the shipping and mariners required for his Majesty's naval service.
" They all declare that the best of their shipping, in respect of the long peace, were sold, and that such that are unsold being of any worth are at their voyages out of the country, and the few remaining that are within the country are only small barks unfurnished of ordnance and unable either to pursue or defend. And, touching the mariners, it was affirmed by them that the greatest number of people of that sort within this kingdom are in the coast side of Fife, who are fishers and presently following their trade of fishing in the Isles, and their return is not looked for afore September, at which time they will be upon their preparation for the Bourdeaux voyage."

28. Burntisland Council. Tuesday 9th July 1633.

Item Ordain all women and bairns in Burntisland bide in their homes from morn to eve under the pain of law…. Imprisoned for 8 days.

Item Ordaineth.. The kings servants who desire to be admitted and made Burgesses and Freemen of the Burgh for the love and favour of the Bailies and Counsel.

29. Burntisland names gleaned from historic record.

First Name	Surname	Title 1	Position
Robert	Cowan		Shipmaster 'William'
Robert	Richardson		Shipmaster
John	Dury		Shipmaster
John	Cairns/Walker		
James	Adamson		Doctor B.Island
John	Anderson		Constable Burntisland.
David	Andrew	Freeman B.Island	Tailor?
Patrick	Angus		Shipmaster 'David'
Archibald	Angus		Skipper
Robert	Archison	Bailie B.island	merchant
Alexander	Barnie		worker/Ferries
John	Boswell		Crew 'Blessing'
James	Brown		Tailor/Ferries
Robert	Brown		Crew 'Blessing'
Robert	Brown		Crew Bosun? Baggage boat
John	Brown	Freeman B.Island	Baker
William	Brown		Bosun ? Baggage Boat.
Thomas	Christie	Master	Schoolmaster B.Island
Elspeth	Coasin		/Ferries
James	Common		Crew Baggage boat
James	Dawson		Shipmaster 'Pilgrim'
Thomas	Dewar	Bailie B.Island	
Robert	Ennand		Crew Baggage boat
George	Gairne		merchant
Robert	Galbraith	Bailie B.Island	
Edward	Garden	Bailie B.Island	
Robert	Gardner		Shipmaster
John	Ged		Shipmaster
John	Goodwin		Crew Baggage boat
John	Gordoun		Crew Baggage boat
Robert	Harroware		Crew Baggage boat
Henry	Henryson		Crew 'Blessing'
Robert	Huggens	Bailie B.Island	
Janet	Mair		/Ferries funeral
John	Man		Shipmaster
William	Marshall	Freeman	
John	Mason		Crew 'Blessing'
William	Meiklejohn		Shipmaster
John	Meldrum	Bailie B.Island	
Sir Robert	Melville		Landowner fife
John	Michaelson		minister St. Columba 1616

William	Mitchell		/Ferries funeral
William	Murchison	Bailie B.Island	
Thomas	Murray	Bailie B.Island	
David	Murray		Crew 'Blessing'
Andrew	Orrock		Gravedigger/ Ferries funeral
James	Orrock		Shipmaster / Baggage boat
Alexander	Patterson	Freeman B.island	maltman
William	Phine		Shipmaster 'Gift of God'
James	Redie		Shipmaster
Robert	Richardson		Shipmaster
Andrew	Seaton		Shipmaster 'Grace'
James	Shaw		Crew 'Blessing'
John	Smith		Crew Bosun? 'Blessing'
David	Stirling		Carpenter/Ferries
James	Wat (elder)		Crew 'Blessing'
James	Wat (yngr.)		Crew Baggage boat
Andrew	Watson	Bailie B.Island	Shipmaster
John	White		Bellringer/Ferries
Robert	Whyte		Crew 'Blessing'
John	Whyte	Burgh Councillor	
Robert	Williamson	B.Islambd?	Crew Baggage boat
Robert	Wilson		Crew Baggage boat
James	Workman		Painter Watson / M.S.house

30. Accounts of the Master of Works (Scotland)   1633

8th July. Item to a boat for carrying of the matting over the water that gaid to Falkland. 20 shillings.

31. Register of the Privy Council (Scotland)

Acta June 1632 - June 1634 Fol. 180,b.

Attending - Stathearn; Privy Seal; Wigton; Ayr; Bishop of Dunblane; Bishop of the Isles; Carnegie; Traquair; Secretary; Clerk Register, Advocate.

Holyrood House 17th January 1633

Appointments of commissioners to superintend the repair of the highways.

The Lords of Secret Council, finding it necessary and expedient for the honour and credit of the kingdom and for his Majesty's contented reception here, that the highways and passages through which his Majesty's progress will lie be mended, helped and enlarged and made passable for coaches and horses, therefore the said Lords have nominated and appointed the persons following within the bounds particular underwritten to ride the said highways and passages and to consider what places need either enlarging or mending of the ways, fords, bridges or passages, and after exact consideration thereof to prescrive and publish the order which they shall find most meet and easy to repair the necessary defects foresaid by the travails and charges of the inhabitants within the said bounds, and the said orders to be to be perfected between the ? day of ? nextcome; and that it be straightway enjoined to the sheriffs and justices of peace to have a care to see that the directions to be given to them and the order and rule to be set down in this business to be performed, and that they render an account of the diligence of the country where they dwell to his Majesty's Council upon the ? day of ? that if anything be resting undone and perfected they who shall be found negligent or undutiful may be censured and punished; and if all of them who are in the commission shall not be present that such of them that are present do that which is enjoined to be performed by the whole; and that the said commissioners report to the Council upon the ? day of ? They're whole proceedings in this matter and of the orders to be set down by them and by the sheriffs and justices of the peace and all that has proceeded therein.

Follows the names of the commissioners nominated and appointed for this service, viz. - ...... for the bounds between Falkland and Burntisland, The Lords Melville, Burleigh and Wemyss, and the Lairds of Balvaird, Balmowto and Balfour.

32. Annals of Scotland J. Balfour
the kingdom had not seen a more glorious sight, the streets being railed and sanded, the chief places where he passed were set out with triumphal arches, obelisks, pictures, artificial mountains adorned with choice music and other diverse costly shows

33. Annals of Scotland   J. Balfour
Those attending his Majesty on his down coming to Scotland.

Title	Number	Servants	Horses
Gentlemen Pensioners	31	93	93
Lord and Bishops.	15	429	678
Govt.	6	38	46
Ushers. Privy Chamber	5	11	13
Gentlemen. Privy Chamber.	8	32	32
Gentlemen Ushers.	3	12	12
Grooms. Bedchamber.	6	30	50
Cup Bearer	2	8	8
Carver.	2	8	8
Sewer	2	8	8
Squire of the Body	2	8	8
Groom. Privy Chamber. Mr. Adrian May.	3	12	12
Sergeant at Arms.	2	6	6
Squires of the Chamber	2	4	4
Chaplains	7	24	24
Medical	7	30	27
Robes. Robert Josley. Yeoman	3	8	8
Beds	10	21	21
Guard.	61	60	60
Crossbows.	25	29	29
Knight Harbinger	1	3	3
Mr. Comptroller	1	25	25
Cooks. Etc.	42		
TOTAL	246	899	1175

34. Rawlinson MS D.49; The gests of the progress to Scotland

The King was royally feasted at Welbeck House at the Earl of Newcastle's where was a standing banquet after dinner amounting to the value of seven hundred pound and after that in the outer court there was a speech made to the King, then a marriage between an exceedingly tall wench and a very low dwarf with quintance and dancing.

35. Scottish Record Office

1633, May 11 - July 22, - The Gist's of His Majesty's Progress to Scotland.

List of the Places and the stay at each. Scotland.

Dunbar	(June 12)	1 night	
Seton	(June 13)	1 night	
Dalkeith	(June 14)	1 night	
Edinburgh	(June 15 - June 30)	16 nights	
Linlithgow	(July 1)	1 night	
Stirling	(July 2 – 3)	2 nights	
Dunfermline	(July 4)	1 night	
Falkland	(July 5 – 9)	5 nights	(Perth July 8)
Edinburgh	(July 10 – July 15)	5 nights	(Leaves July 13)

36. Scottish Record Office.

Account of the provisions brought out of England in the good ship called the 'Blue Doo' of Anstruther of the quantity and weight that follows :

Of pewter 6 great chargers, 3 dozen 7 pound plates weighing – 203 quarters 22 pounds
4 dozen 5 pound plates weighing – 223 pounds
4 dozen 4 pound plates weighing – 103 quarter 2.5 pounds
4 dozen 3 pound plates weighing – 101 quarters 4 pounds
4 dozen 2.5 pound plates weighing – 102.5 pounds
4 dozen 2 pound plates weighing – 3 quarters and 14 pounds
1 pound plates weighing – 1 quarter and 23 pounds
6 long great plates weighing – 1 quarter 26 pounds
12 pottell flagons weighing – 3 quarters 4 pounds
12 gallon flagons weighing – 101 quarters 22 pounds

Total of the weight – 1300 quarters and 7 pounds

37. Accounts of the Master of Works (Scotland)   1633

8th July. Item to Robert Denmuir, smith, for five forks (part of harness), two of them to the king's coach horses, two to his great horse and one to his wagon horses.   1 shilling.

38. Annals of Scotland.   J. Balfour

had cloth of crimson velvet embroidered with gold and oriental pearls, the bosses and bridles being richly set with emeralds, rubies and diamonds…

39. State papers (Domestic)

May 3rd.   Draft of a proclamation concerning King's progress towards Scotland.

Whitehall.

The Kings most Excellent Majesty having taken into his Princely consideration some inconveniences which may fall out, and happen in His intended Journey towards His Kingdom of Scotland, if present care be not had to prevent the same: Hath thought fit by advice from His Privy Council, to publish and declare by this Proclamation; …….
And His Majesty being graciously, and providently careful to prevent such grievances, which may in this journey happen to His loving Subjects, doth likewise hereby straightly charge and command, that none of His Majesty's Servants, nor the servants of any Nobleman, or others whatsoever, shall in the said Journey, presume to take any Cart or Carts, but such as shall be delivered unto him or them, by some one of His Majesty's Cart-takers, or their deputies. ………….

40. State papers (Domestic)

Vol. 232
February 27. 1633 Office of the Ordnance.

Estimates by the Officers of the Ordnance of the charge of 50 fair-carts, with necessary provisions, to attend the King in his journey to Scotland.   Total, £421. 3s.

41. Register of the Privy Council (Scotland)

Acta June 1632 - June 1634 Fol. 189, b.

Charges to sheriffs and magistrates concerning the transportation of his Majesty's baggage.

Attending - Strathearn; Wigton; Lauderdale; Bishop of Dunblane; Bishop of the Isles; Lord Lorne; Lord Erskine; Lord Melville; Traquair; Secretary; Advocate.

In so much as amongst the many preparations which must be timelessly foreseen and in readiness against the time of his Majesty's coming to this kingdom that of his Majesty's carriage is not the least, but does all nearly concern his Majesty's honour and service and credit of the country as any other service that will occur in all his Majesty's progress throughout this country; and whereas this service cannot be done but by the help of the inhabitants of the sheriffdoms through which his Majesty's progress will lie and of the next adjacent parts, as was done the time of his Majesty's late dear fathers coming to this kingdom, therefore the Lords of Secret Council ordains letters to be directed charging the sheriffs of …………, Fife, …….and their deputes, and the conveners of the justices of the peace within the said sheriffdoms, that they and every one of them within their own bounds and offices respective convene the barons and landed gentlemen within their bounds with all convenient diligence and at their meeting that they resolve and conclude upon some certain , solid and sure course how his Majesty's carriage may be carried through their bounds upon his Majesty's charge and expenses, and for this effect that they make a particular distribution of the said sheriffdoms in parishes, appointing some of their number for every parish to try what number of carts and horses for carriage every parish may furnish, and that they appoint a constable for every parish who shall be answerable that carts and horses for carriage designed to every parish shall be in readiness for his Majesty's service as they shall be directed and advertised; and siclike that they nominate and appoint two other constables for every parish who shall have the charge to advertise the constable of the parish to have the carts and horses for carriage in readiness at the times to be appointed; and likewise that they appoint two constables for each sheriffdom who shall be answerable to the Master of his Majesty's carriage that they shall cause the other constables appointed in every parish have the horses and carts for carriage designed to the parish in readiness to come and lift his Majesty's carriage at such times and places as they shall, be advertised and that the said sheriffs, baillies and conveners of the justices of the peace compeer personally before the said Lords upon the   day of March next and make a perfect report in writing of their proceedings in this business, under the pain of rebellion, etc., with certification, etc.

Register of the Privy Council (Scotland)

Royal Letters 1623 -33 Fol. 227a

Holyrood House 31st January 1633

Letter to the justices of the peace concerning provision for the conveyance of his majesty's baggage

After our very hearty commendations. Whereas among other preparations which are now in hand and must be timely foreseen and in readiness against the time of his majesties herecoming that of the carriage is not the least but does nearly concern his majesty's honour and service and the credit of the country as any other service that will occur in all his majesties progress throughout the same, and whereas this service cannot be well done but by the shires where his majesty and journey will lie, as was done when his majesties late dear father of eternal memory was coming to this kingdom, we must therefore lay a part of this service upon you; and for this effect these are to request you to convene the rest of your brethren and justices of the peace within that shire and to advise and resolve among yourselves how and in what manner his majesty's carriage maybe most formally and orderly carried from … to … for ready and thankful payment, or if you will follow the order prescribed by yourselves the time foresaid of his majesty's dearest father his coming to this kingdom that accordingly you will convene the whole brethren of the bench to burgh and land within that sherriffdom so soon as conveniently maybe and make a particular distribution of the said sherriffdom in parishes, appointing some of your number for every parish, to try what number of carts and horses for carriage every parish to burgh and land may furnish for his majesty's carriage upon his majesties expense, and that you appoint a constable in every parish who shall be answerable that the carts and horses for carriage designed to every parish shall be in readiness for his majesty's service when ever they shall be advertised by the principal constable of the shire who shall have the charge of advertisement, and you shall appoint within that sherriffdom two constables who shall be answerable to the masters of his majesty's carriage that they shall cause the other constables appointed to every parish to have the carts and horses for carriage designed to the parish in readiness, and that they shall come and lift his majesty's carriage at such times and places as they shall be advertised and if you find any other course more meet and fit to be followed for the furtherance of this great service nor this, you shall set down your judgment and opinion therein in writ and report the same to his majesty's council upon the 14th day of March next, which , recommending to your care and diligence as a piece of service highly importing the credit of the country we commit you to god From Holyrood House, the last day of January 1633 subscribed Stathearn, Haddington, Winton, Bishop of the Isles, Arch. Acheson

42. Scottish Record Office

E34/52.   Undated bundle relating to Coronation 1633
Sheet of paper listing names concerned with the visit (Culinary)

Cooks : **John Ferris**, Thomas Morris, John Garaway, John Andrews, Robert Lovell, John Aoolee, Joseph _____ , John Keene, John Fevor, John Mushy, Christopher Sherman, Thomas Fletcher, Edward Jones, Walter Billie, Nicholas Lord, Henry Clark, John Buckley, Henry Givine, Thomas Lee, Edward Dyar, Henry Jones, Edward Cragg, Hugh _____ , Jasper _____ ,
Skewers - 4, Turnbroches,
kitchen boy, - 10, Labourers as needed.

43. Register of the Privy Council (Scotland)

Fol. 188b

Sitting - Stathearn; Privy Seal; Bishop of Dunblane; Bishop of the Isles; Erskine; Melville; Traquair;
        Secretary; Advocate; Sir James Baillie

Holyrood House 21st February 1633

Inasmuch as there is a great necessity that sufficient provision be made of straw and hay for furnishing of his Majesty's own equerry and the horse of his train and followers the time of his majesty's coming and remaining in this kingdom, therefore the lords of Secret Council ordain letters to be direct charging officers of arms to pass, fence and arrest the whole straw and hay within the sherriffdoms of Linlithgow, Stirling and Clackmanan and such parts thereof as are nearest To his Majesty's castles of Stirling and palace of Linlithgow and within the regality of Dunfermline and the north side of the Forth and such parts of the sherriffdom of Fife as are nearest To his Majesty's palaces of Dunfermline and Falkland ...., and those within the sherriffdom of Fife nearest to the regality of Dunfermline to the Laird of Pitfirrane, Mr. Thomas Wardlaw and the said David Balfour, or any two of them, who will attend them at the burgh of Dunfermline upon the   day of ; and these within the sherriffdom of Fife nearest to the palace of Falkland to make their address to James Kynninmonth, Chamberlain of Fife, and to the said David Balfour, who will attend them at the burgh of Falkland upon the   day of   ; and at there meetings at the places respective aforesaid that they agree with the persons foresaid who are appointed to attend them as said is upon the price of their said hay and straw, and according to the said agreement they shall receive timely and thankful payment; and that the owners and possessors of the said hay and straw keep the days foresaid in the places respective abovewritten assigned unto them and there attend the persons foresaid who are to agree with then in manner foresaid under pain of rebellion, Etc., with certification etc.

Register of the Privy Council (Scotland)

Acta June 1632 - June 1634 fol. 222, b.

Directions concerning the conveyance of his Majesty's baggage from Falkland to Burntisland.

Attending - Chancellor; Treasurer; St. Andrews; Glasgow; Privy Seal; Winton; Wigton; Lauderdale; Viscount Ayr; Bishop of the Isles; Traquair; Secretary; Clerk of Register; Advocate; Sir James Baillie.

Holyrood House 15th May 1633.

In so much as the convener of the justices of the peace of Fife and Kinross, according to a warrant and direction sent unto them by the Lords of Privy Council, has taken particular notice of the number of horses that every parish within the said sheriffdoms may be conveniently furnished for lifting his Majesty's carriage from Dunfermline to Falkland and from Falkland to Burntisland and has made and presented a roll of the said parishes containing the number of ploughs within every parish and appointing every fotche (double yoked) plough to furnish a cart and two horses where carts are, and two horses where no carts are, and two single ploughs a cart with two horses or two horses for carriage; and they have divided the said sheriffdoms into four presbytery and within every presbytery has appointed general constables, to wit, for the presbytery of St. Andrews, Peter Greg, messenger there, for the presbytery of Cupar, Lawrence Burrell, messenger there, for the presbytery of Dunfermline, Robert Stirk, messenger there, and for the presbytery of Kirkcaldy, James Pitblado, messenger there, who are to charge the particular constables of every parish to advertise the parishioners to have their horses and carts in readiness as they shall be required to that effect. Likewise for this purpose they have appointed the persons underwritten constables in every parish who all have accepted the charge and given up the number of ploughs within each parish in manner following, viz.,

In the presbytery of St. Andrews :

Parish	Constable	Constable	Assessment
Kemback	David Cowper in Dura	Thomas Gibson in Blebohall	8 fotche ploughs
Forgan	John Henderson	John Miller	24 fotche ploughs
Ferry	Thomas Imbrie	James Adam	5 fotche ploughs
Leuchars	William Short	George Greeve	40 fotche ploughs
Largo	William Henderson		20 fotche ploughs
Newburn	David Simpson		11 fotche ploughs
Kilconquhar	John Drummond		31 fotche ploughs, 1 single plough
Abercrombie	John Bedeson		4 fotche ploughs
Carnbee	John Beans	Henry Ramsey	32 fotche ploughs
Kilrenny	Thomas Anderson	James Russell	12 fotche ploughs
The landwart of Crail	Patrick Danskin		19 fotche ploughs
Kingsbarns	William Corstorphine	Alexander Brig	23 fotche ploughs
The landwart of St.Andrews	William Kerr, John Smith	John Miller, William Alexander	50 fotche ploughs
Dunino	William Henderson		6 fotche ploughs

and the burghs following are ordained to furnish the number of horses following, to wit, the burgh of St. Andrews 12 horses, the burgh of Crail 8 horses, Anstruther Wester 3 horses, Anstruther Easter 6 horses, Kilrenny 2 horses, and Pittenweem 3 horses.

For the presbytery of Cupar :

Parish	Constable	Constable	Assessment
Landwart of Cupar Town of Cupar	Robert Balfour in Balgarvie	Alexander Ballingal in Kilmaron	16 fotche ploughs, I single plough 8 carts
Cults	Andrew Daniel of Bunzeoun	Patrick Grundestone in Barblair	9 fotche ploughs
Kettle	William Bettie in Orkie	David Rymour, Kettle	25 fotche ploughs
Falkland	Andrew Burrell	David Strachan	19 fotche ploughs
Strathmiglo	James Ballingall	John Sunzeour in Pitgornoch	20 fotche ploughs
Auchtermuchty	Henry Sim, Auchtermuchty	Michael Gudwillie in Dempstertown	18 fotche ploughs
Collessie	George Scot, Collessie	William Thomson of Newtown	20 fotche ploughs
Ebdie	John Swinton in Grange	John Tod in Burnside	25 fotche ploughs, 1 single plough
Monimail	William Ballingall, Monimail	Robert Morris of Fernie	25 fotche ploughs, 1 single plough
Creich	**James Clark** in Luthrie	Robert Williamson in Balmeadowside	9 fotche ploughs, 1 single plough
Dunbog	Walter Duncan in Johnstown (Ayton?)	John Spittal in Highome	8 fotche ploughs, 1 single plough
Flisk	James Bott at the mill of Ballincreich	Thomas Bowman	11 fotche ploughs
Balmerino	James Bartlett in Kirkton		9 fotche ploughs
Kilmany	John Henderson, Kilmany	Thomas Ramsay in the Starr	24 fotche ploughs, 1 single plough
Logie	Andrew Bell in Denbrae	Alexander Ramsay in Cruvie	12 fotche ploughs, 1 single plough
Auchtermoonzie	David Suntar, Achtermonsie	John Ferrie in Colluthie	6 fotche ploughs, 1 single plough
Dairsie	John Gourlay in Middlefudie	John Walker in Pittormie	15 fotche ploughs, 1 single plough
Sires (Ceres)			31 fotche ploughs, 1 single plough
Newburgh	Patrick Ramsay		10 horses

In the presbytery of Kirkcaldy :

Parish	Constable	Constable	Assessment
Burntisland	**John Anderson**, Burntisland, (burgh)	**Henry Johnstone** in Newbigging, (parish)	26 single ploughs
Kinghorn	William Heich, (burgh)	James Lichton in Pittedie, (parish)	40 single ploughs
Kirkcaldy	James Speidie, Andrew Alexander, (burgh)	David Knox in Tirbene, Thomas Lamb in Raith, (parish)	20 single ploughs
Dysart	Thomas Cokin in Dunikeer		20 single ploughs
Markinch	Andrew Wilson, Markinch	Walter Morgan in Balbirnie	64 single ploughs
Ballingray	John Pudgall in Corshill	Robert Meldrum at Inchegall mill	12 single ploughs
Leslie	James Robertson, Leslie		30 single ploughs
Kinglassie	Thomas Currour in Stenton	Andrew Law in Pitlethie	24 single ploughs
Auchterderran	**Robert Kilgour** in Pitkeny	John Stirk in Balgregie	25 single ploughs
Auchtertool	John Crawford, Auchtertool	Thomas Adestoun in Clentrie	9 single ploughs
Portmooke	Andrew Baith in Kirkness	George Bickartoun in Kinnesswood	21 single ploughs
Kennoway			
Wemyss			
Scoonie			

As likewise the constables of Kirkcaldy give up 12 horses for that burgh; the constables in Dysart 12 horses for that burgh; the constables in Kinghorn 20 horses for that burgh; the constables of Burntisland 20 horses for that burgh.

In the presbytery of Dunfermline :

Parish	Constable	Constable	Assessment
Dunfermline	David Mitchell	James Angus	140 ploughs
Carnock	William Gibbon		20 ploughs
Orruell	Robert Patterson	Harry Livingstone	24 ploughs
Baith	John Orrock		4 ploughs
Aberdour	William Alexander	William Anderson	16 ploughs
Inverkeithing, Rosyth	Mr. John Murray, John Thomson	William Thomson	35 ploughs
Dalgaty	John Henderson		17 ploughs
Torryburn	Andrew Mudie		6 ploughs

As in the report made here at length is contained. And whereas the parishes foresaid who are given up to contain the number of fotche ploughs and single ploughs above written, and every fotche plough to furnish one cart and two horses where carts are, and two horses where no carts are, and two single ploughs one cart with two horses or two horses for carriage, are bound in duty to have their horses and carts and other instruments and necessaries for carriage in readiness at Dunfermline upon the fifth day of July next and at Falkland upon the tenth day of the said month, early in the morning, and there to lift his Majesty's carriage and carry the same from Dunfermline to Falkland and from Falkland to Burntisland, the days respective foresaid, nevertheless the Lords of Secret Council apprehends that some undutiful persons will lie back and shun this service and neither bring nor send their horses to Dunfermline and Falkland for that use, although that nothing is to be craved of them but for ready and thankful payment, so as it is like enough that apart of the carriage shall lie behind, to the discredit and shame of the nation without remedy being provided; therefore the said Lords ordain letters to be directed, charging the parishioners of the whole parishes above written and constables appointed for every parish and the general constables of the presbyteries, that they and every one of them do and perform that which to their charge and duty in the service foresaid appertains; and for this effect that they direct and send and cause the number of carts and horses above specified appointed and allowed for every parish, well furnished with all things necessary for carriage, to be at the burgh of Dunfermline upon the fifth day of July next and at the town of Falkland upon the said tenth day of July next before three oft the clock in the morning and there to lift his Majesty's carriage and carry the same from Dunfermline to Falkland and from Falkland to Burntisland respective upon his Majesty's charges and expenses, under the pain of six pounds for every horse that shall be absent and shall not come in due and lawful time to lift his Majesty's carriage, as said is, and further under the pain to be punished in their persons as disappointers of his Majesty's service at the arbitrement of his Majesty's Council; And suchlike to command and charge the general constables of the said presbyteries to poind the readiest goods and gear of the persons disobeying for the said sum of six pounds for every horse that shall be absent and shall not keep the precise time and place of their meeting at the sight and discretion of the master of the carriage, and to make the said some further commend to those whom the said Lords shall appoint in this errand. And suchlike to command and charge the constables of each parish to bring with them and to deliver to the master of the carriage a list and roll of the number of horses that shall be absent, to the intent that the owners of the absent horses may be punished for their failure and disobedience by poinding for the said six pounds, as said is; certifying the said constables who shall not give up the said list and roll in manner foresaid that they and every one of them shall incur the said pain of six pounds for every absent horse or not given up by them as absent and shall be poinded for the same accordingly. And suchlike to command and charge the sheriffs of Fife and Kinross and the conveeners of the justices of the peace within the same and provost and baillies of the burghs foresaid that they within their several bounds, offices and jurisdictions have a special care they the particular constables of every parish, do and perform all and everything which to their several charges appertains as they will answer upon the dutiful discharge of their offices.

44. Five Articles of Perth.

1st, That the Eucharist should be received in a kneeling, and not in a sitting posture; 2nd, That the sacrament should be given to the sick at their own house when they were in danger of death; 3rd, That baptism should, in like cases, be administered in private houses; 4th, that the youth should be confirmed by the bishops; and 5th, That the festivals of Christmas, Good Friday, Easter, Ascension Day, and Whitsunday, should be observed in Scotland just as in England.

45. Histoire of the Church of Scotland. Row.

….. In the week following, the Lords of the Articles daily sat, and the King came up daily from the Palace and sat with them. At which time, the commissioners both of barons and burgesses were inhibited by the King to have any meeting contrary to the form practised in all other parliaments before: Whereat they conceiving a fear that matters should not go right, and hearing that the Lords of the Articles had concluded among them sundry things that were an evident hurt both to Kirk and country, they penned a Supplication which was to be subscribed by many both of the Nobility, Barons and Burgesses, to be delivered to the King before the last day of the Parliament; yet the matter being known they were prevented; and this Supplication, was not given in at that time, yet the number of them was well known in their votes in open Parliament. ......

Contrary to many men's expectations, and before this Supplication could be subscribed by so many as were willing so to do, the Parliament rose and ended on Friday the 23rd of June : and when the Articles came to be voted, the King, perceiving that there would be some contrary to them, takes pen and with his own hand noted the votes, whereby, no doubt, many were afraid to vote according to their conscience.

Some of the Nobility voted especially against the Articles concluded concerning Church business, but would have consented to other Articles concerning Annual Rents and such things; yet being all put to together, they behoved to vote against all or consent to all. My Lord Melville, an aged and good nobleman, said, both wisely and gravely,

"I disagree from these Articles concluded against the former order of this Kirk, because your Majesty's father, of good memory, after he had sworn himself, caused me and all the kingdom to swear and subscribe to The Confession of Faith that was then set down; wherein all these things that now are rejected by our Kirk!"

Which speech made the King pause awhile, but he could make no answer.

in end, what by the King's acting the part of the Clerk, to overawe the Parliament; what by his sharp speeches to sundry of the well affected Nobility and gentry; what by proxies and other the like means, by plurality of votes, all the Articles concluded by the Lords of the Articles were concluded also in open Parliament. But the negative votes were thought by some to have equalled the affirmative; and a worthy gentleman (Lord Rothes) stood up and quarrelled with the Clerk Register (Sir John Hay) for not marking the votes rightly: But the King, who also had marked them himself, the like whereof was not practised to the knowledge of any living, commanded the gentlemen to be silent, or else upon the peril of his life make that good which he had spoken: whereupon the gentleman sat down and was silent.

46. "Sir John Hay, The Incendiary" John A Inglis. Scottish Historical Review. No. 15. 1917.

..... The incident opened the whole question of the rights of strangers, especially Englishmen, to fish off the Scottish coast, and on the 11th November 1630, the King, on the narrative that foreigners had been reaping the benefit of ' the great blessing wherewith it has pleased god to enrich his Majesty's dominions of Scotland, England and Ireland in the abundance and plenty of fish upon all coasts,' appointed six commissioners for Scotland, including John Hay, to confer with six English representatives, with a view to founding a fishing association for control of the whole industry. The Scots proposed that the fishings off their coasts should be closed to all except Scotsmen, and as their English colleagues objected to the proposal, John Hay was sent to report the matter to the Royal Burghs for their suggestions. The Burghs supported the proposal and suggested a fourteen-mile limit all round the coast. The point was referred to the King, who replied that he could not understand the necessity for such a reservation, and that he could only reserve to natives 'such fishing without which they cannot well subsist, and which they of themselves have and do fully fish.'

A Royal Charter was signed on 19th July 1632, erecting a company with a council of twelve - six to represent Scotland, John Hay being one, and six to represent England and Ireland. Hay's efforts were rewarded with a knighthood, and on 19th October 1632, he and four of his colleagues appeared before the Privy Council at Edinburgh to report the result of their negotiations. They mentioned that 'his Majesty, out of his royal and princely regard of the honour, credit and wealth of this his ancient kingdom, honoured almost the whole meetings for this treaty with his royal presence'; and they were thanked by the Council, who entered on their Register a finding that they had 'very honourably and faithfully carried themselves therein for the honour, credit and wealth of this kingdom.' The next stage of Sir John Hay's career was reached on 12th December 1632, when he was appointed Clerk Register. Sir

James Balfour's comment upon the appointment was, that he was 'one altogether corrupt, full of wickedness and villainy, and a sworn enemy to the peace of his country.

47. Annals of Scotland. Sir James Balfour.

… But it proved in the end a forcible rope to draw the affections of the subject from the Prince.

To be short, of 31 Acts and Statutes concluded in this Parliament, not three of them but were most hurtful to the liberty of the subject; and as it were also many partitions to separate the King from his people. This Parliament was led one by the Episcopal and court faction, which thereafter proved to be that stone that afterwards crushes them to pieces, and the jewel of that flame which set all Britain afire not long thereafter. In this Parliament, his Majesty noted up the names of such as voted against the three former acts, with his own hand, wherein he expressed now and then a great deal of spleen; this unseemly act of his Majesty bred a great heart burning in many, against his Majesty's proceedings and government.

48. Papers of Sir Hervey Bruce.   1617   Extract

" A discourse or Description of his Majesty's Entertainment in Scotland, and of that Land"

".. First, for the country, I must confess 'tis too good for those that inhabit it, and too bad for others to be at the cost to compare it. The air might be wholesome but for the stinging people that live in it, and the ground made fruitful had they the wit to manure it. Their beasts are small (weame , *belly*, excepted) of which sort their is no greater in the world. Their is great store of fowls, as foul houses, foul linen, foul dishes and pots, foul trenchers and napkins, foul sheets and shirts, with which sort of fowl we had like to have fared as the children of Israel did with their fowl in the wilderness. They have great store of fish, and good for those that can eat it raw, but if it once come into their hands, 'tis presently three days old. For their butter and cheese I'll not meddle with it this time, nor no man at any time that loves his life. They have likewise great store of deer, but they are so far from the places where I have been, that I had rather believe it than go to disprove it. I confess all the deer I met withal was dear lodgings, dear horsemeat, dear tobacco, and English beer. As for fruit, for the grandame Eve's sake they never planted any, and for other trees, had Christ been betrayed in this country (as doubtless he should have been had he come as a stranger amongst them) Judas had as soon found the grace of repentance, as a tree to <have> hanged himself on. They have many mountains, wherein they tell me is much treasure, but they show none of it : nature has only discovered unto them some mines of coals, to show to what end she created them.   I see little grass, but in their porridge; and no flowers, but such as modesty forbids me to name. The thistle was not given them for nothing, for it is the fairest flower in their garland. The word hay is heathen Greek to them; neither man nor beast knows what it means. Their fellows are their followers, their wives their slaves, their horses their masters <mistresses>, and their swords their judges, by reason whereof there are but few lawyers, and they not rich. Their parliaments hold but three days, their statutes are in three lines, and a suit is determined in three words. The wonders of the kingdom are these : The Lord Chancellor is loved and honoured; the Master of the Rolls is well spoken of; and the whole Council (who are the judge of all causes) are free from suspicion of corruption

The country, though it be mountains, affords no monsters but women, of which the great ones, as countesses and ladies, are kept like lions in iron grates; the merchants' wives are likewise prisoners, but not kept in such strong holds. They have wooden cages like English boarfranks, *enclosure*, through which sometimes peeping to catch the eye, we are sometimes choked with the sight of them. The greatest madness amongst the men is jealousy, in that they fear to lose what no man that has but two of his senses will seek to get. The ladies are of that opinion, that Susanna could not be chaste of her body because she bathed so often. Pride is a thing naturally bred in their bones; and their flesh naturally abhors cleanliness. Their breaths commonly stink of porridge; their linen of piss, their hands of pigs' turds, and their whole bodies of sweat. Their splay feet never offend in wearing of socks. To be chained in marriage to one of them, were to be tied to a dead carcass, and cast into a stinking ditch. The ointment most frequent amongst them is brimstone and butter for their scabs, and oil of bays and stavesaker for their lice, which sin of curiosity is but newly crept into their kingdom, and I think will not long continue.

49. Rawlinson Papers. Bodleian Lib.

The Gists of the Progress to Scotland with other observations in the journey.

The country is very fruitful for thorns ………for the rest the most is barren and generally all…..
In this country women change not their names by marriage but their children are called by their father's name.
Likewise they bury with no funeral but bring them to the graveyard under ….. in all put of them beneath and ….. a …..
there till then art shall and so seem them to be buried by the Lord.

50. Rev. Field Collection. H.M.C.

July 10th 1633. High Sheriff's Writ to the Chief Constables of the hundred of Martinsley Whereas appointment is given by the Lords of his Majesty's most honourable Privy Council to me Anthony Colly, Knight, sheriff of this county, to provide horses to attend his Majesty's return from Scotland : These are therefore in his Majesty's name straightly to charge and command you that presently upon the receipt hereof you take order to provide twenty of the best sufficient able horses with good sufficient saddles and bridles, and able men for guides for to carry the horses to Post Witham, to be ready to attend his Majesty upon Friday morning between 7 and 8 of the clock, which shall be the 19th day of this present month.

51. State Papers. Venetian.

July 22nd 1633. Vicenzo Gussoni, Venetian Ambassador in England, to the Doge and Senate.

The king has left Edinburgh, both the people and his Majesty having given and received mutual satisfaction, as well in the parliament as in everything else. He wished to proceed to Stirling and Falkland to enjoy the hunting and have the pleasure of seeing the country in which he says he is proud of being born, although he left it as a baby of two.
The last session of that parliament voted an extraordinary contribution of six portions, payable to his Majesty in six years, to the amount of 120,000 pounds sterling. This is the more gratifying to the king because he knows that added to the others, it is more in proportion with their affection than their means, as the nation in general has no superfluity of money.

52. Papers   Sir John Coke

July 2nd. 1633. Richmond. - Lord Goring (to Sir John Coke).

My cousin Tom Weston arrived here with extraordinary diligence last night which was the third after his departure from Edinburgh. Her Majesty hath commanded me to send away her four coaches so as they may be at their several stages on the 13th of this present, the first whereof will be at Huntingdon, and so on to Greenwich.

53. State Papers. Venetian

August 5th 1633. Vicenzo Gussoni, Venetian Ambassador in England, to the Doge and Senate.

The king has accelerated his journey extraordinarily by relays of coaches at several places, after the manner of the posts. By this haste he wished to take the queen by suprise, so as to make his return more welcome to her when she was not expecting him, although she awaited him with impatience when he tarried before for the space of some days. The Duke of Lennox, the Marquis of Hamilton, and three other great lords, no more, attend on his Majesty on this very hurried and almost flying journey. The Lord Treasurer, the Earl Marshal and others of the Council and Court have remained behind and will come by easier stages with the rest of the cavaliers and officials of the usual company that follows the king.

54. Register of the Privy Council (Scotland)

Acta June 1632 - June 1634 fol. 186a

attending - Stathearn; Privy Seal; Winton; Wigton; Bishop of Dunblane; Erskine; Iles; Secretary;

Advocate.   Holyrood House 12th February 1633

Inasmuch as one **Robert Tough** of Dysart, being of late prisoner in the Poultry of London for certain sums of money due by him, did, under pretence to use his means to pay his creditors , intreat John Atkinson, door keeper of the said prison, to go abroad with him to that effect, as is ordinarily accustomed there, but having escaped and ran away from his keeper to this kingdom to shelter himself here from the due course of justice, whereby he is like to undo his keeper in being made liable by his escape to pay the debt, and to defraud his creditors of what is justly due unto him (sic); which being contrary to the due course of justice which mutually ought to be kept amongst all his majesty's loving subjects and an act in him worthy of censure and punishment, therefore the Lords of Secret Council, according to a warrant and direction in writ signed by the kings Majesty and this day exhibited unto them , ordain letters to be directed to messengers of arms charging them to pass , search , seek and take the said Robert Tough wherever he can be apprehended, and to bring, present and exhibit him before his Majesty's Council....

Bibliography

The majority of Government records, Privy Council, Domestic, Venetian were researched through the published volumes available at major Libraries. A large number of collections were sourced through the published volumes of the Historic Manuscripts Commission. Where necessary original manuscripts were accessed at The British Library, Scottish Records Office, Somerset Records Office and Traquair House.

Balfour J: Annals of Scotland,
Bass G F: A History of Seafaring, Thames and Hudson 1972
Jackson G: Ports (The History and Archaeology of), World's Work 1983
Kenyon J P: Stuart England, Pelican 1985
Lamont-Brown R: Discovering Fife, John Donald Publishers 1988
Lavery B: Susan Constant (The Colonial Merchantman), Conway Maritime Press 1988
Marshall R: Henrietta Maria (the Intrepid Queen), HMSO 1990
Mayer A: Annals of European Civilization, Cassell 1949
Morgan K O: The Tudors and Stuarts, Oxford University Press 1992
Prebble J: The Lion in the North, Penguin 1981
Robertson A S: The Antonine Wall, Glasgow Archaeological Society 1970
Row J: History of the Kirk of Scotland from 1558-1637,
Rubinstein W D: Wealth and Inequality in Britain, Faber and Faber 1986
Sharpe K: Charles I (The Personal Rule of), Yale University Press 1992
Smith A G R: The Emergence of a Nation State, Longman 1984
Snoddy T G: Sir John Scotstarvit, Constable 1968
Spalding J: History of the Troubles and Memorable Transactions of Scotland,1624-1645, Spalding 1792
Tincey J: The Armada Campaign 1588, Osprey 1988
Weir M: Ferries in Scotland, John Donald Publishers 1988
Magnusson M: Biographical Dictionary, Chambers 1990
Hydrographic dept. MOD: North Sea (West) Pilot, Hydrographer of the Navy 1973

About the Author

Howard Murray, whose family have a long association with Fife, was educated at St. Andrews. He started his professional career in the Antiquities Department of Dundee City Museums in the early 70's and played a major part in the archaeological rescue projects of the medieval Scottish Burghs before moving South, then abroad. His work in Norway led to a position in Belfast developing conservation freeze-drying techniques. His subsequent success at the Mary Rose Project, where he developed and led the Organics Conservation team from 80 –84, allowed him to return to Scotland. The conservation and project management company he started in Dundee did not survive the 80's. He now works as *Archaetexture*, a self-employed consultant in the Heritage Industry.

ACKNOWLEDGEMENTS

Thanks are due to Frank Baird, for editing and literary assistance; to Eric Bell of Cluny for the cover illustration, to Alex Kilgour for chasing the publishing side and the rest of the team for keeping going and keeping me going.

Regarding the quest for historical data, thanks are due to Bob Brydon, Martin Rhydderch and Alex Kilgour of the Project Team for additional research and support and the late Professor Donaldson, Histographer Royal for Scotland, for being a light in the halls of Academia. I am also indebted to the following: St Andrews University Library, Hay Fleming Library, Scottish Record Office, British Library, Somerset Record Office, Traquair House, Lady Hesketh (Bodleian Library). Special thanks also to Keith Wickham, Chairman of Silverscreen Print Plc who has kindly reduced the print cost for this publication to help raise funds for the Project.

Illustration Sources

Plate 1: Charles I on Horseback, Van Dalen. Windsor Castle
Plate 2: Falkland Palace, Slezor. National Library of Scotland
Plate 3: Chart Firth of Forth, M Downie.
Plate 4: View of Burntisland, Slezor. National Library of Scotland
Plate 5: Andrew Troughton Note. Traquair House
Plate 6: JewelHouse Records, Mildmay Papers. Somerset Records Office
Colour Plate 1: Dutch East Indies Fleet, Van Ertvelt. National Maritime Museum
Colour Plate 2: Duke of Hamilton, Myten. Scottish National Portrait Gallery
Colour Plate 3: Charles I, Scottish National Portrait Gallery
Colour Plate 4: Map of Burntisland. British Library
Illustration Pages 19/29:
Illustration Pages 25/32:
Illustration Pages 27/48:

King Charles Shipwreck Quest
Under the auspices of Burntisland Heritage Trust.
An Interview with Ian Archibald.

Following the withdrawal of a US exploration group, Burntisland Heritage supported a local proposal to continue the search for a Historic Wreck, the ferryboat that sunk off Burntisland on 10th July 1633. After carrying out further historic research, a team was set up by Ian Archibald. The past months have seen some interesting developments. Here he answers some questions.

Who are involved? We are working with the original Scottish team comprising Alex Kilgour and the marine archaeologists and historians. For our search I initially involved Carl Galfskiy, a fellow member of Kirkcaldy Sub Aqua Club. Carl works offshore as a Remote Operated Vehicle pilot and supervisor. His technical expertise has been invaluable. Mark Blyth and friends from Burntisland Watersports have greatly assisted with regular marine support and facilities. Rab Wise is an engineer who lent a hand with the metal detection surveys. George Penn is a lifeguard and dive leader at the dive club. We have also had tremendous technical support from Matt Blair of Tritech International Ltd.; an Aberdeen based company specialising in sonar equipment. Commander Bob Stewart, Officers and Crew of HMS Roebuck were also valuable in their support. On the fringe of all the hi-tech and in parallel with the main project I tested the skills of Jim Longton a map dowser from Lancashire.

What about yourself? I live in Burntisland and work as a Cartographic Manager in Edinburgh. My survey and mapping experience spans back thirty-five years. When I first heard the story of the shipwreck it really captured my imagination. After all it's not every day you hear of part of a Royal baggage train sinking on your own doorstep. In 1992 I instigated a local support group which later became Burntisland Heritage. In 1997 I realised that for us to have a positive future would very much depend on what happened out on the water. I turned my attention to the resurrection of the search and formed a locally based project team.

What exactly are you looking for? There are many recorded sinkings of ships in the Forth but only a few would qualify as historic wrecks. I would be happy to find any of these. The one that sunk in 1633 was a comparatively small wooden ferryboat. The remains of the vessel could be buried in the mud and silt. It is unlikely that any of this will protrude above the seabed. It is probable however that the remains will lie quite close to the surface beneath a scour or mound that is very small. There will also be some metal content, which is detectable.

How can you find it? We are concentrating on one area at a time starting in a place the American team did not search. They took all the data back with them and its unlikely to emerge again. At the moment I am following through on a clue that came from additional historical research. So far we have used side scan, image and bottom profiling sonar in conjunction with a magnetometer for metal detection.

Have you found anything yet? After surveying an area of specific interest using all the equipment just mentioned, a target that matched many of the requirements was located. It was the right size on sonar print outs and recorded a low metal reading. In November 1998 this target was confirmed as being a wooden shipwreck.

How do you know it's wooden? A sub-bottom survey was carried out using leading edge technology. Confirmation has also come from team divers Carl Galfskiy and Mark Blyth.

What's it like down there? It is very demanding diving. The biggest problem for us is very poor visibility. Sometimes you can barely see your hand in front of your face. If you let go of the line it's like being lost in space! Even the most powerful torches make no difference. There is also the added problem of strong tidal currents, which limit the diving opportunities.